THE OFFICIAL CHARTS' MUSIC QUIZ BOOK

Official
Charts Company

THE OFFICIAL CHARTS' MUSIC QUIZ BOOK

Lee Thompson

Michael O'Mara Books Limited

First published in Great Britain in 2022 by Michael O'Mara Books Limited

9 Lion Yard
Tremadoc Road
London SW4 7NQ

ISBN: 978-1-78929-501-6 in paperback print format

1 2 3 4 5 6 7 8 9 10

www.mombooks.com

Front cover photography: Billie Eilish: © Paul Fenton / ZUMA Wire / Alamy, Kate Bush: Trinity Mirror / Mirrorpix / Alamy, Stormzy: Kaylum Dennis, The Beatles: Pictorial Press Ltd / Alamy
Back cover photography: Beyoncé: PA Images / Alamy, Ed Sheeran: Tony @ Black Ink
Designed by Natasha Le Coultre
Typeset by Barbara Ward

Printed and bound by CPI Group (UK) Ltd, Croydon, CR0 4YY

The Official Charts® have been a central part of British popular culture for 70 years and counting. With our finger on the throbbing pulse of the British record-buying, digital-downloading, music-streaming public, the Official Charts are the UK's only official, trusted weekly barometer of what's popular in music right now.

As heard on BBC Radio 1, *Top Of The Pops* and MTV, the Top 40 Official Singles Chart has been chronicling the tastes of arguably the most influential music nation on the planet since the very first UK singles chart in November 1952. From The Beatles to Beyoncé, The Rolling Stones to Rihanna, Kylie to Miley, and Spice Girls to Little Mix, the Official Chart has crowned artist success week in, week out, across seven glittering decades.

Whether it is Blur and Oasis locking horns in 1995, the Sex Pistols' *God Save The Queen* controversially being held off Number 1 during the Queen's Jubilee in 1977, or Rage Against The Machine taking on the *X Factor* in 2009's greatest Christmas Number 1 battle in history – the Official Charts aren't just the authority on what is popular in Britain, the Official Charts *are* British pop culture.

Lee Thompson grew up in the north-east of England and became obsessed with music during his formative years in the 1970s. His vinyl collection grew out of hand through his teens and into his twenties, as did his obsession for chart facts and trivia. A love of radio led him to making his own shows in his bedroom in the eighties before becoming a presenter in the nineties at various stations including one of the first incarnations of London's influential indie Xfm. He later worked as Head Of Music at TV music channels The Box, Kiss, Q, Kerrang! Smash Hits, Magic, and The Hits.

Today, he's a consultant and curator of shows on the NOW 70s, 80s, and 90s music TV channels, has produced chart rundown specials with both Gary Davies and Scott Mills at BBC Radio 2, and more than 100 weekly editions of 'Sounds Of The 70s'. He's a self-confessed retro *Top Of The Pops* nerd and loves a good music quiz much more than his wife does. He lives in London.

FOREWORD

**I am very proud to be the brand new host of
The Official Chart show on BBC Radio 1!**

The Official Singles Chart is now in its 70th year and, despite the
seismic shifts in music consumption, the chart has always remained
strong as the only place to truly gauge the most popular music of the
last seven days. I am taking over as host at an incredibly exciting time,
when a song from 40 years ago or from a band no one has heard of
can become Number 1! Of course, while this has always been possible
(who can forget Rage Against The Machine as Christmas Number 1 in
2009 with *Killing In The Name*?), the wider availability of almost every
piece of music ever recorded means it is more common than ever.

The obsession with the charts runs deep through a generation
and this is the perfect book to really test who stayed up taping
the rundown – offering quizzes to test your mates and trivia
to impress your nan. It is a must-have for any chart head!

Jack Saunders

September 2022

*Tune in to The Official Chart on BBC Radio 1 with Jack Saunders
every Friday from 4pm to discover chart history as it happens.*

INTRODUCTION

Let's be honest, who doesn't love a good music quiz?

Whether it's testing your level of expertise against a bunch of mates in your social circle, outwitting siblings during a family gathering, or trying your luck down the pub once a week with daft team names like 'Quiz Team Aguilera', 'Quizzy Rascal', or 'Quiz Team, The Strawberry Girl, Quiz Team, Banana Split Lady' (bit of a niche one for the Goths, that), everyone plays to win once that competitive instinct kicks in.

I've been writing and compiling music quiz questions ever since I was a kid, so when the team at the mighty Official Charts asked if I fancied pulling together a book stuffed full of pop brain-teasers and head-scratchers, I couldn't resist. It's been a proper labour of love.

There's something here for you if you followed the weekly ins and outs of the Official Singles and Albums Charts at any time from the 1950s to the 2020s, either briefly or obsessively. You're among friends here, for sure. I'm convinced that nobody on the planet will know the answer to literally every question, but I would love to hear from you if you come maybe even 80% close!

Within these pages, you'll find themed quizzes loosely based around a topics or a common words that crop up time and time again in hit songs. There are also individual questions on every month from January 1980 to December 2021, plus an Official Singles Chart

Top 10 from each of those years where we've cunningly blanked out several artists and titles, just to see how good your nerdy knowledge really is. Plus, there's plenty more to keep you amused.

It wasn't that long ago that my dad told me he used to write down the weekly chart from Radio Luxembourg on a Sunday night when he was a teenager in the fifties, straining to keep up as the signal faded in and out. He was oblivious to the fact that I'd discreetly been doing the same thing with Radio 1's Tuesday lunchtime new chart reveal for many years, and continued doing so when things flipped to a Sunday night with Bruno Brookes in September 1987. There was obviously something in the genes.

This book is for anyone else like me and my dad. Chances are that at some point in your life you cherished seven-inch singles that you'd bought with your spare pocket money and then wore them out by playing them endlessly. If your formative years were during the cassette single era or the CD boom, when Saturday in Woolworths meant you'd gaze at the wall racks to find your favourite, the same applies. Oh, and you too if you're a millennial or Generation Z-er who always had your iPod primed to download the week's big new tunes every Monday morning, ready for your journey to school, college, or work.

Long live the charts and, to misquote the late, great Olivia Newton-John on her 1981 anthem, let's get quizzical.

Lee Thompson

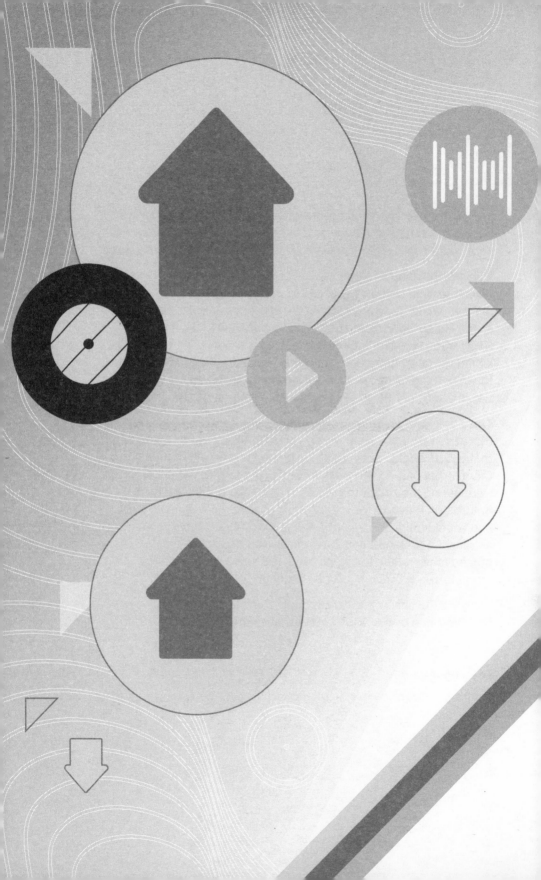

QUESTIONS

STARTING TOGETHER

Congratulations if you knew that this opening quiz section has the same title as Su Pollard's only hit, and that it reached Number 2 in February 1986 – this book is going to be right up your street!

Let's ease you in gently, though, with a set of bands and artists that we've mashed together because the last part of one name is the first part of the other. All of them have had at least one hit during the first 70 years of the Official Singles Chart.

Find the single word link for each of the 40 different pairings:

1. Simply (___) Hot Chili Peppers

2. Boyz II (___) At Work

3. Joss (___) Roses

4. Cilla (___) Eyed Peas

5. Doja (___) Stevens

6. Deborah (___) Styles

7. Sean (___) Simon

8. Spice (___) Aloud

9. Buddy (___) Valance

10. James (___) Swift

11. LF (___) Of A Down

12. Paloma (___) No More

13. Billy (___) Corry

14. Swing Out (___) Sledge

15. Break (___) Gun Kelly

16. Livin' (___) Division

17. Tina (___) And Eddie

18. Cathy (___) Waterman

19. James (___) Conley

20. Crowded (___) Of Pain

21. Peggy (___) Dorsey

22. Chase And (___) Quo

23. Calum (___) Walker

24. Kings Of (___) Jackson

25. George (___) Bolton

26. Fountains Of (___) Wonder

27. Ricky (___) Garrix

28. Jimmy (___) Friedman

29. Pseudo (___) And The Bunnymen

30. Viola (___) Boys

31. Sak (___) Harrison

32. Culture (___) Nouveau

33. Frankie Goes To (___) Beyond

34. Ryan (___) Hilton

35. Rufus (___) Dolby

36. All About (___) Boswell

37. Iggy (___) Will Eat Itself

38. Kelly (___) Osmond

39. Carly (___) Park Orchestra

40. Mari (___) Pickett

Answers on page 248

COME TOGETHER

Quite often, it's good to know you have a solid backing group of friends behind you, rather than going it alone on a hit record. Sometimes you're the front person for the whole band and get the main attention ahead of the others. Or maybe even your name is just a daft play on words.

Whatever the case, here are 40 examples of '... And The ...' acts from the Official Singles Chart.

So who's missing?

1.   ___ ___ And The Wailers
2.   ___ ___ And The Miracles
3.   ___ And The Plastic Population
4.   ___ And The Family Stone
5.   ___ ___ And The Pips
6.   ___ And The Waves
7.   ___ ___ And The Teenagers
8.   ___ And The Dominos
9.   ___ ___ And The Blockheads
10.   ___ And The Medics
11.   ___ And The Makers
12.   ___ ___ And The Blue Notes
13.   ___ And The Diamonds
14.   ___ And The Pan
15.   ___ ___ And The Stingers
16.   ___ ___ And The Tremeloes
17.   ___ ___ And The Sunshine Band
18.   ___ ___ And The Coconuts
19.   ___ ___ And The Smurfs
20.   ___ ___ And The Commotions
21.   ___ ___ And The News

22. ___ And The Delrons

23. ___ ___ And The Bruvvers

24. ___ ___ And The Pirates

25. ___ ___ And The Vandellas

26. ___ ___ And The Dipsticks

27. ___ ___ And The Modern Lovers

28. ___ ___ And The Rebel Rousers

29. ___ ___ And The Sex-O-Lettes

30. ___ ___ ___ And The Get Fresh Crew

31. ___ ___ And The Drells

32. ___ And The Mechanics

33. ___ And The Dreamers

34. ___ ___ And The Range

35. ___ ___ And The Boyz

36. ___ ___ And The Blackhearts

37. ___ And The Pacemakers

38. ___ ___ And The Shondells

39. ___ ___ And The Replays

40. ___ ___ And The Mastermixers

Answers on page 248

MILLION SELLERS

Each of these songs is a confirmed UK million-selling hit according to the Official Charts Company, with their tallies comprising actual physical singles and/or download sales.

We've listed 20 titles plus the year that they first arrived on the Official Singles Chart in brackets.

Who are the bands and artists responsible for these musical milestones?

1. *I Will Survive* [1979]

2. *Ghostbusters* [1984]

3. *What Makes You Beautiful* [2011]

4. *I Don't Want To Miss A Thing* [1998]

5. *Tie A Yellow Ribbon Round The Ole Oak Tree* [1973]

6. *Ride On Time* [1989]

7. *Thinking Out Loud* [2014]

8. *Somebody That I Used To Know* [2012]

9. *The Carnival Is Over* [1965]

10. *Bright Eyes* [1979]

11. *Torn* [1997]

12. *Save Your Kisses For Me* [1976]

13. *Blue (Da Ba Dee)* [1999]

14. *That's My Goal* [2005]

15. *I'd Like To Teach The World To Sing (In Perfect Harmony)* [1971]

16. *The Lion Sleeps Tonight* [1982]

17. *Don't You Worry Child* [2012]

18. *Fight For This Love* [2009]

19. *Stranger On The Shore* [1961]

20. *Think Twice* [1994]

Answers on page 248-9

HIT AFTER HIT:
THE ROLLING STONES

Place these five **ROLLING STONES** hits in their correct chronological order as they each appeared on the Official Singles Chart.

A. LET'S SPEND THE NIGHT TOGETHER

B. JUMPIN' JACK FLASH

C. UNDERCOVER OF THE NIGHT

D. HARLEM SHUFFLE

E. MISS YOU

Answers on page 249

ONE TO FIVE:
THE KINKS

Each of these **KINKS** hits achieved a different peak position on the Official Singles Chart. Put them in the correct order, starting with Number 1 and working your way down to Number 5.

A. DEDICATED FOLLOWER OF FASHION

B. LOLA

C. AUTUMN ALMANAC

D. APEMAN

E. SUNNY AFTERNOON

Answers on page 249

HIT AFTER HIT:
DIANA ROSS

Place these five **DIANA ROSS** solo hits in
their correct chronological order as they each
appeared on the Official Singles Chart.

A. WHY DO FOOLS FALL IN LOVE?

B. TOUCH ME IN THE MORNING

C. I'M STILL WAITING

D. UPSIDE DOWN

E. LOVE HANGOVER

Answers on page 249

ONE TO FIVE:
CLIFF RICHARD

Each of these **CLIFF RICHARD** hits achieved a
different peak position on the Official Singles Chart.
Put them in the correct order, starting with
Number 1 and working your way down to Number 5.

A. DADDY'S HOME

B. WE DON'T TALK ANYMORE

C. SOME PEOPLE

D. SANTA'S LIST

E. WIRED FOR SOUND

Answers on page 249

THE FIFTIES

These are the biggest-selling singles in the UK during the 1950s, according to the Official Charts Company, ranked from Number 1 to Number 10. Can you name the nine* acts who gave us these huge songs from the early days of the Official Singles Chart?

(*One artist features twice here)

1. *Rock Around The Clock* [Number 1 in November 1955]

2. *Diana* [Number 1 in August 1957]

3. *Mary's Boy Child* [Number 1 in November 1957]

4. *What Do You Want To Make Those Eyes At Me For?* [Number 1 in December 1959]

5. *Jailhouse Rock* [Number 1 in January 1958]

6. *What Do You Want?* [Number 1 in December 1959]

7. *Living Doll* [Number 1 in July 1959]

8. *All Shook Up* [Number 1 in July 1957]

9. *Love Letters In The Sand* [Number 2 in August 1957]

10. *It Doesn't Matter Anymore* [Number 1 in April 1959]

Additionally, how many names can you correctly match to this list featuring ten of the decade's Number 1 song titles?

11. *Magic Moments* [Number 1 in February 1958]

12. *Secret Love* [Number 1 in April 1954]

13. *Sixteen Tons* [Number 1 in January 1956]

14. *Rose Marie* [Number 1 in July 1955]

15. *Who's Sorry Now?* [Number 1 in May 1958]

16. *Look At That Girl* [Number 1 in September 1953]

17. *Hoots Mon* [Number 1 in November 1958]

18. *Softly Softly* [Number 1 in February 1955]

19. *A Woman In Love* [Number 1 in October 1956]

20. *Yes Tonight Josephine* [Number 1 in June 1957]

Answers on page 249

ELVIS PRESLEY

1. Elvis Presley made his Official Singles Chart debut in 1956 with which song?

2. Name the 1957 hit that gave Elvis his first Official Singles Chart Number 1.

3. In 1982, an Elvis classic made its way into the Top 40 thanks to a live version, which featured him laughing uncontrollably throughout – which song was it?

4. In total (including his 2005 re-issues), how many Number 1s has Elvis Presley had on the Official Singles Chart?

5. Presley's 1972 Top 10 hit *Always On My Mind* was revived by Pet Shop Boys for an ITV tribute show and became the Christmas Number 1 in what year?

6. Each of these Elvis hits achieved a different peak position on the Official Singles Chart – put them in the correct order, starting with Number 1 and working your way down to Number 5.

   a. *Suspicious Minds*
   b. *A Big Hunk O' Love*
   c. *My Boy*
   d. *(Let Me Be Your) Teddy Bear*
   e. *Wooden Heart*

Answers on page 249

NUMBER 1 MILESTONES

We've listed 18 landmark moments since the birth of the Official Singles Chart, beginning with the first ever Number 1 through to the 1400th. Next to a performer or group, you'll see the missing number of words from each title, plus the month and year that they made it to the top of the chart. How many of these songs can you correctly name?

1:   Al Martino – ___ ___ ___ ___ [November 1952]

100:   Anthony Newley – ___ ___ ___ [April 1960]

200:   The Beatles – ___ [August 1965]

250:   The Union Gap featuring Gary Puckett – ___ ___ [May 1968]

300:   Dawn featuring Tony Orlando – ___ ___ ___ [May 1971]

400:   Julie Covington – ___ ___ ___ ___ ___ [February 1977]

500:   Nicole – ___ ___ ___ [May 1982]

600:   T'Pau – ___ ___ ___ ___ [November 1987]

700:   Chaka Demus & Pliers featuring Jack Radics and Taxi Gang – ___ ___ ___ [January 1994]

750:   Robson & Jerome – ___ ___ ___ ___ ___ ___ / ___ ___ ___ ___ ___ / ___ ___ ___ ___ (*officially listed as a triple-A-sided hit) [November 1996]

800:   All Saints – ___ ___ [September 1998]

900:   Christina Aguilera, Lil' Kim, Mya, and P!nk – ___ ___ [June 2001]

1000:   Elvis Presley – ___ ___ / ___ ___ ___ (*officially listed as a double-A-sided reissue) [January 2005]

1100:   Cascada – ___ ___ ___ [July 2009]

1200:   will.i.am featuring Eva Simons – ___ ___ ___ [July 2012]

1250:   Clean Bandit featuring Jess Glynne – ___ ___ [February 2014]

1300:   Rachel Platten – ___ ___ [September 2015]

1400:   Eliza Rose & Interplanetary Criminal – ___ ___ ___ ___ (___ ___ ___ ___) [September 2022]

Answers on page 249

HIT AFTER HIT:
CHER

Place these five **CHER** hits in their correct
chronological order as they each appeared
on the Official Singles Chart.

A. GYPSYS, TRAMPS AND THIEVES

B. ONE BY ONE

C. THE MUSIC'S NO GOOD WITHOUT YOU

D. STRONG ENOUGH

E. I FOUND SOMEONE

Answers on page 249

ONE TO FIVE:
STEVIE WONDER

Each of these **STEVIE WONDER** hits achieved a
different peak position on the Official Singles Chart
– put them in the correct order, starting with Number 1
and working your way down to Number 5.

A. FOR ONCE IN MY LIFE

B. I JUST CALLED TO SAY I LOVE YOU

C. HAPPY BIRTHDAY

D. MY CHERIE AMOUR

E. I WISH

Answers on page 249

BACK TO THE SIXTIES

Next, here's a great selection of songs, comprising many of the decade's biggest sellers from famous stars, and a few of the other coolest, grooviest hits from the Official Singles Chart during this incredible period in music.

Each band or artist is only represented once on this list of 60 records.

How many can you name?

1.   *Good Vibrations* [Number 1 in November 1966]

2.   *Get Off Of My Cloud* [Number 1 in November 1965]

3.   *A Whiter Shade Of Pale* [Number 1 in June 1967]

4.   *River Deep, Mountain High* [Number 3 in July 1966]

5.   *Halfway To Paradise* [Number 3 in August 1961]

6.   *Mr. Tambourine Man* [Number 1 in July 1965]

7.   *Cathy's Clown* [Number 1 in May 1960]

8.   *Telstar* [Number 1 in October 1962]

9.   *I Got You Babe* [Number 1 in August 1965]

10.   *In The Year 2525* (Exordium And Terminus) [Number 1 in August 1969]

11.   *Louie Louie* [Number 26 in February 1964]

12.   *Son Of A Preacher Man* [Number 9 in January 1969]

13.   *You Really Got Me* [Number 1 in September 1964]

14.   *(There's) Always Something There To Remind Me* [Number 1 in October 1964]

15.   *Ob-La-Di, Ob-La-Da* [Number 1 in January 1969]

16.   *Hit The Road Jack* [Number 6 in November 1961]

17.   *(Sittin' On) The Dock Of The Bay* [Number 3 in March 1968]

18.   *Walkin' Back To Happiness* [Number 1 in October 1961]

19.   *Itchycoo Park* [Number 3 in September 1967]

20.   *Wichita Lineman* [Number 7 in March 1969]

21. *See Emily Play* [Number 6 in July 1967]

22. *A Boy Named Sue* [Number 4 in October 1969]

23. *Distant Drums* [Number 1 in September 1966]

24. *Save The Last Dance For Me* [Number 2 in December 1960]

25. *Too Busy Thinking 'Bout My Baby* [Number 5 in September 1969]

26. *Like A Rolling Stone* [Number 4 in September 1965]

27. *Runaway* [Number 1 in June 1961]

28. *Reach Out I'll Be There* [Number 1 in October 1966]

29. *Go Now!* [Number 1 in January 1965]

30. *Sugar, Sugar* [Number 1 in October 1969]

31. *The Last Waltz* [Number 1 in September 1967]

32. *I Remember You* [Number 1 in July 1962]

33. *White Room* [Number 28 in February 1969]

34. *It's Getting Better* [Number 8 in October 1969]

35. *You've Lost That Lovin' Feelin'* [Number 1 in February 1965]

36. *The House Of The Rising Sun* [Number 1 in July 1964]

37. *Wild Thing* [Number 2 in May 1966]

38. *Build Me Up Buttercup* [Number 2 in December 1968]

39. *Twistin' The Night Away* [Number 6 in April 1962]

40. *Let's Twist Again* [Number 2 in February 1962]

41. *La Mer (Beyond The Sea)* [Number 8 in February 1960]

42. *Hang On Sloopy* [Number 5 in October 1965]

43. *Respect* [Number 10 in July 1967]

44. *Get Ready* [Number 10 in March 1969]

45. *Leader Of The Pack* [Number 11 in February 1965]

46. *MacArthur Park* [Number 4 in July 1968]

47. *My Old Man's A Dustman* [Number 1 in March 1960]

48. *Where Do You Go To (My Lovely)* [Number 1 in February 1969]

49. *Out Of Time* [Number 1 in July 1966]

50. *Glad All Over* [Number 1 in January 1964]

51. *For Your Love* [Number 3 in April 1965]

52. *Bad Moon Rising* [Number 1 in September 1969]

53. *Be My Baby* [Number 4 in November 1963]

54. *Daydream Believer* [Number 5 in January 1968]

55. *She's Not There* [Number 12 in September 1964]

56. *Born To Be Wild* [Number 30 in July 1969]

57. *Then He Kissed Me* [Number 12 in October 1963]

58. *For Once In My Life* [Number 3 in January 1969]

59. *My Generation* [Number 2 in November 1965]

60. *Hey Jude* [Number 1 in September 1968]

Answers on page 250

SUPERSTAR SPOTLIGHT:

1. How many Number 1s did the group achieve on the Official Singles Chart during the 1960s – and how many Number 1s did they have on the Official Albums Chart that same decade?

2. Which Number 1 song by The Beatles became the biggest-selling single of the 1960s?

3. *Love Me Do* was the band's first hit on the Official Singles Chart, peaking at Number 17, but it later came back and reached Number 4 – in what year was that re-issued song much bigger second-time around?

4. Name the newly recorded Beatles song that reached Number 2 in 1995 and saw the three surviving members reunited, now working with producer Jeff Lynne from E.L.O.

5. Which of the four Beatles was the first to score a solo Number 1 on the Official Singles Chart?

6. Place these ten hits by The Beatles in their correct chronological order as they each appeared on the Official Singles Chart during the 1960s.

   a. *A Hard Day's Night*
   b. *The Ballad Of John & Yoko*
   c. *From Me To You*
   d. *I Want To Hold Your Hand*
   e. *All You Need Is Love*
   f. *Please Please Me*
   g. *Ticket To Ride*
   h. *Paperback Writer*
   i. *Lady Madonna*
   j. *Can't Buy Me Love*

Answers on page 250

HIT AFTER HIT:
DONNA SUMMER

Place these five **DONNA SUMMER** hits in
their correct chronological order as they each
appeared on the Official Singles Chart.

A. LOVE'S UNKIND

B. I FEEL LOVE

C. STATE OF INDEPENDENCE

D. THIS TIME I KNOW IT'S FOR REAL

E. DINNER WITH GERSHWIN

Answers on page 250

ONE TO FIVE:
THE BEE GEES

Each of these **BEE GEES** hits achieved a different
peak position on the Official Singles Chart – put
them in the correct order, starting with Number 1
and working your way down to Number 5.

A. YOU WIN AGAIN

B. STAYIN' ALIVE

C. HOW DEEP IS YOUR LOVE?

D. YOU SHOULD BE DANCING

E. DON'T FORGET TO REMEMBER

Answers on page 250

THE FIRST TIME

All these tunes were debut Top 40 hits for some very familiar bands and artists.

In brackets, we've listed the month and year that each song first appeared on the Official Singles Chart.

Just name the 20 acts who were credited on each of these titles. Oh, and several of them had songs that missed the Top 40 before the song that's listed here, but these are the ones that properly kickstarted their careers.

1.   *Roxanne* [May 1979]

2.   *Ms Jackson* [March 2001]

3.   *Cannonball* [December 2011]

4.   *Sultans Of Swing* [March 1979]

5.   *Dreams* [May 1998]

6.   *Hot Dog* [February 1980]

7.   *Harder To Breathe* [January 2004]

8.   *This Charming Man* [November 1983]

9.   *Shiver* [March 2000]

10.   *Stay* [October 1993]

11.   *New Life* [July 1981]

12.   *Rehab* [October 2006]

13.   *Supersonic* [April 1994]

14.   *There You Go* [June 2000]

15.   *I Know Where It's At* [September 1997]

16.   *Kiss On My List* [November 1980]

17.   *Run* [February 2004]

18.   *Nothing Can Divide Us* [September 1988]

19.   *Last Request* [July 2006]

20.   *Breathe Again* [January 1994]

Answers on page 250-1

CLOSE BUT NO CIGAR

It's one of those great expressions that's used when something narrowly misses its target, and it was even the inspiration behind the title of a Number 22 hit by Thomas Dolby in May 1992.

The phrase certainly applies to these 20 fantastic songs from the first three decades of the Official Singles Chart. They all really deserved to have been Number 1, but got stuck at Number 2 instead.

So who sang them?

1. *You Sexy Thing* [November 1975]

2. *Solid Gold Easy Action* [January 1973]

3. *Love Is The Drug* [November 1975]

4. *Heartbreak Hotel* [June 1956]

5. *Young Hearts Run Free* [July 1976]

6. *Oliver's Army* [March 1979]

7. *Downtown* [December 1964]

8. *Rasputin* [October 1978]

9. *Cool For Cats* [April 1979]

10. *Love Really Hurts Without You* [March 1976]

11. *Yesterday Once More* [August 1973]

12. *My Boy Lollipop* [May 1964]

13. *All Right Now* [July 1970]

14. *Flowers In The Rain* [October 1967]

15. *The Jean Genie* [January 1973]

16. *Wake Up Little Susie* [December 1957]

17. *You Ain't Seen Nothing Yet* [December 1974]

18. *The Loco-Motion* [October 1962]

19. *This Town Ain't Big Enough For Both Of Us* [June 1974]

20. *Crazy Horses* [November 1972]

Answers on page 251

HIT AFTER HIT:
OLIVIA NEWTON-JOHN

Place these five **OLIVIA NEWTON JOHN** hits in their correct chronological order as they each appeared on the Official Singles Chart.

A. HOPELESSLY DEVOTED TO YOU

B. IF NOT FOR YOU

C. PHYSICAL

D. A LITTLE MORE LOVE

E. SAM

Answers on page 251

ONE TO FIVE:
ELTON JOHN

Each of these **ELTON JOHN** hits achieved a different peak position on the Official Singles Chart – put them in the correct order, starting with Number 1 and working your way down to Number 5.

A. ROCKET MAN

B. NIKITA

C. CROCODILE ROCK

D. ARE YOU READY FOR LOVE

E. SONG FOR GUY

Answers on page 251

70 FROM THE SEVENTIES

How well do you know the music and stars from the decade that brought us prog rock, glam, disco, country, punk, new wave, and so much more? Let's find out.

1. *Rhinestone Cowboy* was a Top 5 hit in November 1975 for which country music star?

2. Name the former member of The Beatles who scored a solo Number 1 for five weeks in January and February 1971 with *My Sweet Lord*.

3. *The Funky Gibbon* reached Number 4 in April 1975 for which TV comedy trio?

4. What two-word title gave Roxy Music their debut hit on the Official Singles Chart in August 1972?

5. Who asked the question *Is She Really Going Out With Him?* on his Top 40 debut in August 1979?

6. In what year did David Cassidy reach Number 1 with the song *How Can I Be Sure*?

7. How many Number 1s did Led Zeppelin achieve on the Official Albums Chart during the seventies?

8. Name the 1974 debut hit on the Official Singles Chart for The Commodores.

9. *Come Back My Love*, *The Boy From New York City*, and *It's Raining* were all consecutive Number 2 hits during 1978 for which group?

10. Name the song that spent three weeks at Number 1 during the Summer of 1976 for Liverpool band The Real Thing.

11. Where did Typically Tropical say they were going to on their Number 1 song in August 1975?

12. Which prog-rock supergroup trio had a Number 1 on the Official Albums Chart in June 1971 with *Tarkus*?

13. *Billy Don't Be A Hero* was a Number 1 on the Official Singles Chart in March 1974 for which Nottingham-based band?

14. Lulu covered which David Bowie song and took it into the Top 3 in February 1974?

15. Name ABBA's 1979 Number 1 on the Official Albums Chart, which contained the hit singles *I Have A Dream*, *Does Your Mother Know*, and *Chiquitita*.

16. What was the title of the 1977 debut hit on the Official Singles Chart for the band Heatwave?

17. *Blockbuster* was the only Number 1 song for which glam-rock group?

18. Between which two American cities was Patsy Gallant heading on the title of her Top 10 song in October 1977?

19. Leo Sayer made his Official Singles Chart debut in December 1973 with which song?

20. The March 1976 Number 2 hit *Love Really Hurts Without You* was a debut hit for which male solo star?

21. Name the Carole King album that was released in 1971 and then went on to spend a total of 93 weeks on the Official Albums Chart during the seventies.

22. *Breakfast In America* was a 1979 Top 10 song on the Official Singles Chart and was also the title track of a Top 10 LP on the Official Albums Chart for which group?

23. Which band had two Number 1 hits during 1975 with *Bye Bye Baby* and *Give A Little Love*?

24. *You're The First, The Last, My Everything* was a Number 1 song in December 1974 and the biggest-ever hit for which legendary performer?

25. Who sang about the exploits of a saucy *Telephone Man* on her Top 10 hit in September 1977?

26. Wizzard scored two Number 1 songs during 1973 – the first was *See My Baby Jive*, but what was the second?

27. *Lucky Number* reached Number 3 in March 1979 and was the Top 40 debut for which female musician?

28. *You're So Vain* peaked at Number 3 in February 1973 for which singer?

29. What planet were Boney M taking a *Nightflight To*, according to the title of their 1978 Number 1 on the Official Albums Chart?

30. Name the first Official Singles Chart Number 1 hit for 10cc.

31. *Cool For Cats* and *Up The Junction* both reached Number 2 in 1979 for which band?

32. Perry Como's biggest hit of the seventies on the Official Singles Chart was also the title of his 1973 Number 1 on the Official Albums Chart – name it.

33. What was the title of the first Official Singles Chart Number 1 hit for Slade?

34. Motown star Diana Ross collaborated with another legendary label-mate in 1974 for the Top 5 duet *You Are Everything* – who was he?

35. *Run For Home* was a Top 10 comeback hit in the summer of 1978 for which Geordie group?

36. Billy Connolly's 1975 Number 1 *D.I.V.O.R.C.E.* was a parody of a Top 20 hit that same year on the Official Singles Chart – who was the legendary country star who sang that original version?

37. *I Love The Sound Of Breaking Glass* was an April 1978 Top 10 hit for which musician?

38. Liverpudlian four-piece Our Kid won ITV talent contest *New Faces* in May 1976 and landed their only Official Singles Chart entry just a few weeks later with a song that eventually reached Number 2 – what was its title?

39. Who claimed he was *Gonna Make You An Offer You Can't Refuse* on his Top 10 hit in March 1973?

40. The songs *The Day The World Turned Day-Glo*, *Identity*, and *Germ Free Adolescents* all reached the Top 30 in 1978 for which band?

41. Dolly Parton made her Official Singles Chart debut in 1976 and scored her only solo UK Top 10 hit of entire career as a performer – name that tune.

42. *Atom Heart Mother* and *Wish You Were Here* were both Number 1s on the Official Albums Chart during the seventies for which band?

43. Name the Glaswegian singer who scored a surprise Number 1 on the Official Singles Chart in October 1979 with the song *One Day At A Time*.

44. Who claimed *My Resistance Is Low* on his Top 3 hit in June 1976?

45. Which duo said *Welcome Home* on their debut hit that reached Number 1 in July 1973?

46. Donna Summer made her Official Singles Chart debut in January 1976 with which song?

47. Who was *A Punk Rocker*, according to the title of the 1977 Official Singles Chart debut by The Ramones?

48. In what year was the song *Whispering Grass* a Number 1 hit for Windsor Davies and Don Estelle as the characters Battery Sgt Major Williams and Gunner 'Lofty' Sugden from the BBC1 sitcom *It Ain't Half Hot Mum*?

49. Who was treating us all to a slice of *Jungle Rock* on their Top 3 hit in May 1976?

50. Scottish group Middle Of The Road made their Official Singles Chart debut with a song that then spent five weeks at Number 1 in June and July 1971 – what was its title?

51. *Airport* was a July 1978 Top 5 hit for which band?

52. *Sugar Baby Love* was an Official Singles Chart debut in May 1974 that went all the way to Number 1 for which group?

53. *Sticky Fingers* spent a total of five weeks at Number 1 on the Official Albums Chart in 1971 for which great British band?

54. Vicky Leandros won the 1972 Eurovision Song Contest and then scored a Number 2 hit in May 1972 with the English-translated version of the song, now titled *Come What May* – what country did she represent?

55. Name the singer who died in August 2022 and made her Official Singles Chart debut in March 1971 with the Bob Dylan song *If Not For You.*

56. The September 1974 Top 10 hit *Queen Of Clubs* was the debut entry on the Official Singles Chart for which American group?

57. How many Number 1s on the Official Albums Chart did Status Quo achieve during the seventies?

58. *Rock Me Gently* reached Number 2 in October 1974 for which Canadian musician?

59. What was the title of the 1979 song that became the only Top 10 hit for The Skids?

60. Who could hear *Laughter In The Rain*, according to the title of his 1974 Chart Top 20 hit?

61. *Convoy* was a Number 2 hit in March 1976 for which performer?

62. Which British rock band reached the Top 20 for the first time in February 1979 with *Take On The World*?

63. Name the Spanish duo who said *Yes Sir, I Can Boogie* on their Number 1 hit in October 1978.

64. Which comedian scored the 1971 Christmas Number 1 on the Official Singles Chart with the tale of *Ernie (The Fastest Milkman In the West)*?

65. The Police scored two Number 1 hits in 1979 – the first was *Message In A Bottle*, but what was the second?

66. Which group asked us when there'll be a *Harvest For The World* on their Top 10 hit in August 1976?

67. Shortly after Jimi's death, which song by The Jimi Hendrix Experience went to Number 1 on the Official Singles Chart in November 1970?

68. *Annie's Song*, the Number 1 hit from October 1974 by John Denver, returned to the Top 3 in July 1978, thanks to an instrumental version by which famous flautist?

69. In July 1977, Hot Chocolate scored their only Number 1 of their entire career on the Official Singles Chart with which song?

70. In what year did the song *Sweet Caroline* first arrive inside the Top 10 for Neil Diamond?

SUPERSTAR SPOTLIGHT:
DAVID BOWIE

1. How long was the gap between *Space Oddity* first appearing on the Official Singles Chart and it finally reaching Number 1?

2. Which 1972 Mott The Hoople hit was gifted to them by David Bowie as he was a fan of the band and wanted to help them out, rather than see them split up?

3. David scored both his first and second Number 1s on the Official Albums Chart in 1973 – name those two titles.

4. Two of Bowie's Number 1 hits on the Official Singles Chart in the eighties were collaborations – name the acts he teamed up with.

5. What was the title of David's final Number 1 album, released just two days before his death in January 2016?

6. Place these five seventies hits by David Bowie in their correct chronological order as they each appeared on the Official Singles Chart during that decade.

    a. *Life On Mars?*
    b. *Sound And Vision*
    c. *Starman*
    d. *Boys Keep Swinging*
    e. *Golden Years*

Answers on page 252

LONDON SONGS

England's capital city has inspired many hit songs on the Official Singles Chart throughout the decades.

Cast an eye down this list featuring 20 London-themed titles and try to name as many of the acts as you can.

1.   *London Calling* [Number 11 in January 1980]

2.   *Baker Street* [Number 3 in April 1978]

3.   *West End Girls* [Number 1 in January 1986]

4.   *Take Me Back To London* [Number 1 in September 2019]

5.   *Chelsea Dagger* [Number 5 in September 2006]

6.   *Ladbroke Grove* [Number 3 in October 2019]

7.   *London Nights* [Number 2 in July 1989]

8.   *Streatham* [Number 9 in March 2019]

9.   *Finchley Central* [Number 11 in June 1967]

10.   *The Only Living Boy In New Cross* [Number 7 in May 1992]

11.   *Last Train To London* [Number 8 in December 1979]

12.   *(I Don't Want To Go To) Chelsea* [Number 16 in April 1978]

13.   *Camden Town* [Number 14 in October 1995]

14.   *London Bridge* [Number 3 in September 2006]

15.   *Hot Shot Tottenham!* [Number 18 in May 1987]

16.   *Electric Avenue* [Number 2 in February 1983]

17.   *Streets Of London* [Number 2 in January 1975]

18.   *Waterloo Sunset* [Number 11 in March 1997]

19.   *LDN* [Number 6 in October 2006]

20.   *Down In The Tube Station At Midnight*
      [Number 15 in November 1978]

HIT AFTER HIT:
BONEY M

Place these five **BONEY M** hits in their correct chronological order as they each appeared on the Official Singles Chart.

A. MA BAKER

B. MARY'S BOY CHILD

C. SUNNY

D. RASPUTIN

E. RIVERS OF BABYLON

Answers on page 252

ONE TO FIVE:
SHOWADDYWADDY

Each of these **SHOWADDYWADDY** hits achieved a different peak position on the Official Singles Chart – put them in the correct order, starting with Number 1 and working your way down to Number 5.

A. WHEN

B. DANCIN' PARTY

C. PRETTY LITTLE ANGEL EYES

D. UNDER THE MOON OF LOVE

E. I WONDER WHY

Answers on page 252

TRUE COLORS

Cyndi Lauper used the American spelling of the word for her Number 12 hit in October 1986, but it inspired us to find 20 bands or solo artists that each have a colour in their name.

All of them have had at least one Top 20 hit on the Official Singles Chart during its first 70 years, and just to give you some extra help, there are, in fact, only nine different colours spread across the whole list.

How many can you complete?

1. Deacon (___)

2. (___) Floyd

3. (___) Sabbath

4. The Average (___) Band

5. Jocelyn (___)

6. Kissing The (___)

7. (___) Sauce

8. The (___) Crowes

9. (___) Juice

10. (___) Magic Orchestra

11. Karyn (___)

12. (___) Rebel Motorcycle Club

13. 3 Colours (___)

14. Deepest (___)

15. Frijid (___)

16. The (___) Stripes

17. Shocking (___)

18. Cee Lo (___)

19. (___) Grape

20. (___) Oyster Cult

Answers on page 252

HIT AFTER HIT:
SLADE

Place these five **SLADE** hits in their correct chronological order as they each appeared on the Official Singles Chart.

A. MY FRIEND STAN

B. FAR FAR AWAY

C. RUN RUNAWAY

D. CUM ON FEEL THE NOIZE

E. COZ I LUV YOU

Answers on page 252

ONE TO FIVE:
ROD STEWART

Each of these **ROD STEWART** hits achieved a different peak position on the Official Singles Chart – put them in the correct order, starting with Number 1 and working your way down to Number 5.

A. YOU'RE IN MY HEART

B. YOU WEAR IT WELL

C. HAVE I TOLD YOU LATELY

D. EVERY BEAT OF MY HEART

E. THIS OLD HEART OF MINE

Answers on page 252

SPOTLIGHT:
1980s

MONTH BY MONTH: 1980

All data below refers to positions achieved on the Official Singles Chart or (where relevant) the Official Albums Chart.

JANUARY: Which group began the decade by saying *I'm In The Mood For Dancing* on their Top 10 hit?

FEBRUARY: Which New York punk legends scored their only Top 10 entry with *Baby, I Love You*, a cover of the 1963 Number 4 hit by The Ronettes?

MARCH: Name the Top 10 hit that gave Martha and The Muffins their one and only appearance on the Official Singles Chart.

APRIL: Which 1959 song by The Coasters was then a minor hit for The Paramounts in 1964 before mod-revivalists The Lambrettas had the most successful version, reaching Number 7?

MAY: The lyrics to The Undertones' Top 10 hit *My Perfect Cousin* mention a Sheffield band who were yet to appear on the Official Singles Chart, but who then made their Top 40 debut a year later – name that group.

JUNE: The song *Jump To The Beat* debuted on the Top 40 and was the only hit for which teenage singer?

JULY: Which famous six-word quote from William Shakespeare's play *Hamlet* was also the title of a Top 20 hit for B.A. Robertson?

AUGUST: Grace Jones made her Official Singles Chart debut covering a song that The Pretenders recorded on their first album – name that Top 20 hit for Grace.

SEPTEMBER: Ray Dorset wrote Kelly Marie's Number 1 hit *Feels Like I'm In Love*, but with which band did Ray score his own Number 1 as lead singer in 1970?

OCTOBER: The song *Woman In Love* went to Number 1 and became the only chart-topping single for which music icon?

NOVEMBER: Dennis Waterman reached the Top 3 with the song *I Could Be So Good For You*, which was the theme tune from which popular ITV series?

DECEMBER: Name the US rockabilly trio who made their debut on the Official Singles Chart with the Top 10 hit *Runaway Boys*.

TOP 10: 22 MARCH 1980

Fill in the blanks from this complete Official Singles Chart Top 10. If the song title is listed, we're looking for the band or artist that's missing. If the band or artist is listed, we're looking for the missing song title.

1. (NEW) .... GOING UNDERGROUND / DREAMS OF CHILDREN

2. (1) FERN KINNEY ....

3. (3) MARTI WEBB ....

4. (8) THE VAPORS ....

5. (14) .... DANCE YOURSELF DIZZY

6. (4) .... GAMES WITHOUT FRONTIERS

7. (2) .... ATOMIC

8. (20) .... WORKING MY WAY BACK TO YOU / FORGIVE ME GIRL (MEDLEY)

9. (5) .... ALL NIGHT LONG

10. (7) CAPTAIN AND TENNILLE ....

Answers on page 253

All data below refers to positions achieved on the Official Singles Chart or (where relevant) the Official Albums Chart.

JANUARY: The song *Rabbit* was a Top 10 hit for which cockney duo?

FEBRUARY: Fred Wedlock landed a surprise Top 10 novelty hit describing the woes of middle-age – what was the song title.

MARCH: Roxy Music scored their only Number 1 single with a cover of which John Lennon song?

APRIL: *Good Thing Going* was a Number 4 hit for Sugar Minott – which former *EastEnders* actor covered the song and took it back into the Official Singles Chart in 2000, shortly after leaving the show?

MAY: *Swords Of A Thousand Men* spent a fortnight at Number 6 and became the biggest hit for which group?

JUNE: Who scored their second of three 1981 Top 10 hits with the song *I Want To Be Free*?

JULY: Which band gave Jacques Offenbach's 1885 *Can Can* a fresh, ska-influenced twist and landed themselves a Top 3 hit single?

AUGUST: Scottish singer Mary Sandeman adopted what alias on her Number 1 hit *Japanese Boy*?

SEPTEMBER: After being away from the Top 40 since 1975, a song with a one-word title put veteran musician Alvin Stardust back on the Official Singles Chart – name that 1981 hit.

OCTOBER: A cover version of *It's My Party* spent four weeks at Number 1 for producer Dave Stewart and which singer?

NOVEMBER: Who declared it was *A Good Year For The Roses* on their Top 10 hit?

DECEMBER: Name the duo who followed up their Top 3 song *Under Your Thumb* with their next Official Singles Chart hit *Wedding Bells*.

TOP 10: 20 JUNE 1981

Fill in the blanks from this complete Official Singles Chart Top 10. If the song title is listed, we're looking for the band or artist that's missing. If the band or artist is listed, we're looking for the missing song title.

1. (1) SMOKEY ROBINSON ....

2. (3) .... *ONE DAY IN YOUR LIFE*

3. (2) KATE ROBBINS & BEYOND ....

4. (22) .... *TEDDY BEAR*

5. (6) CHAMPAIGN ....

6. (8) .... *GOING BACK TO MY ROOTS*

7. (5) .... *STAND AND DELIVER*

8. (9) .... *WILL YOU*

9. (10) .... *ALL STOOD STILL*

10. (7) .... *YOU DRIVE ME CRAZY*

Answers on page 253

MONTH BY MONTH: 1982

All data below refers to positions achieved on the Official Singles Chart or (where relevant) the Official Albums Chart.

JANUARY: After scoring the 1981 Christmas Number 1 with *Don't You Want Me*, The Human League's next Top 10 hit was a re-issued song that referenced the cultivation of silkworms – name that hit.

FEBRUARY: Who were the first band from Germany to score a Number 1 single on the Official Singles Chart?

MARCH: *Go Wild In The Country* was the first of two Top 10 hits for which band?

APRIL: The 1972 Top 10 hit *Layla* made an unexpected return to the Official Singles Chart, thanks in part to its reissue as a 12" single for the very first time – under what alias did Eric Clapton record the song?

MAY: Jim Diamond sang lead vocals on PhD's Top 3 single *I Won't Let You Down*, but can you name Jim's 1984 solo Number 1 hit?

JUNE: Junior's Top 10 song *Mama Used To Say* was sampled in 2000 for a new Top 3 hit titled *Mama – Who Da Man*? which was recorded by Junior's nephew, but can you name him?

JULY: Queen had a Top 20 hit with a song that had a four-word title in Spanish – what was the track?

AUGUST: *Stool Pigeon* was the second of three Top 10 hits on the Official Singles Chart for which group?

SEPTEMBER: Who was the featured credited vocalist on the song *Walking On Sunshine*, the Top 10 hit for Rocker's Revenge?

OCTOBER: Tears For Fears made their Official Singles Chart debut with which song?

NOVEMBER: The theme song to an ITV mini-series set in Belfast put Clannad on the Top 40 for the first time – name it.

DECEMBER: A 1977 recording of *Little Drummer Boy* mashed up with *Peace On Earth* from a Christmas TV special became an unlikely festive Top 3 smash – the hit saw David Bowie team up with which music legend?

Answers on page 253

TOP 10: 28 AUGUST 1982

Fill in the blanks from this complete Official Singles Chart Top 10. If the song title is listed, we're looking for the band or artist that's missing. If the band or artist is listed, we're looking for the missing song title.

1. (1) DEXY'S MIDNIGHT RUNNERS AND THE EMERALD EXPRESS ....

2. (2) SURVIVOR ....

3. (13) .... WHAT

4. (6) .... CAN'T TAKE MY EYES OFF YOU

5. (27) .... SAVE A PRAYER

6. (3) .... FAME

7. (26) THE KIDS FROM FAME FEATURING VALERIE LANDSBURG ....

8. (4) .... DON'T GO

9. (12) TOTO COELO ....

10. (33) .... NOBODY'S FOOL

Answers on page 253

All data below refers to positions achieved on the Official Singles Chart or (where relevant) the Official Albums Chart.

JANUARY: Men At Work started a three-week run at Number 1 with *Down Under*, but can you name the Australian producer who teamed with the band's original singer, Colin Hay, for a 2022 drum & bass reworking of the song, sending it back into the Top 5?

FEBRUARY: *Na Na Hey Hey Kiss Him Goodbye* put Bananarama back on the Official Singles Chart, but which studio-based US group recorded the original 1970 Top 10 hit version of the song?

MARCH: Name the Australian band who got stuck at Number 17 for three weeks with the song *Hey Little Girl*.

APRIL: Which TV and radio presenter took the track *Snot Rap* into the Top 10?

MAY: Name the singer from Ohio whose song *Love Town* debuted straight inside the Top 20 on the Official Singles Chart.

JUNE: What was JoBoxers' follow-up hit to their Top 3 debut *Boxer Beat*?

JULY: Rod Stewart scored his sixth and final Number 1 on the Official Singles Chart with which song?

AUGUST: Gary Byrd & The GB Experience had a Top 10 hit with a 12" release that ran for more than 10 minutes – what was the song title?

SEPTEMBER: *Dolce Vita* was the only hit song for which Italian singer?

OCTOBER: Men Without Hats debuted on the Official Singles Chart and then reached Number 6 with which song?

NOVEMBER: Following the split of Yazoo earlier in the year, Vince Clarke's next project was The Assembly – who sang vocals on their only hit, *Never Never*?

DECEMBER: Who reached the Top 20 with a reworking of the 1981 Meat Loaf album track *Read 'Em And Weep*?

TOP 10: 15 OCTOBER 1983

Fill in the blanks from this complete Official Singles
Chart Top 10. If the song title is listed, we're looking for
the band or artist that's missing. If the band or artist
is listed, we're looking for the missing song title.

1. (1) .... KARMA CHAMELEON

2. (9) .... THEY DON'T KNOW

3. (4) SIOUXSIE & THE BANSHEES ....

4. (2) .... MODERN LOVE

5. (13) .... NEW SONG

6. (5) PUBLIC IMAGE LTD ....

7. (15) .... IN YOUR EYES

8. (3) .... RED RED WINE

9. (10) NEW ORDER ....

10. (8) .... TAHITI

Answers on page 254

All data below refers to positions achieved on the Official Singles Chart or (where relevant) the Official Albums Chart.

JANUARY: John Lennon was back inside the Top 10 with another posthumous hit – what was the song's three-word title?

FEBRUARY: Under what alias did Kennedy Gordy, the son of Motown Records founder Berry Gordy, make his Official Singles Chart debut with the song *Somebody's Watching Me*?

MARCH: *Your Love Is King* was the debut Top 40 hit for which act?

APRIL: Who scored their first Top 10 hit with *Wood Beez (Pray Like Aretha Franklin)*?

MAY: Which duo were fighting *Love Wars* according to the title of their Top 20 hit?

JUNE: Which group landed their third and final Top 10 entry with the song *Dancing With Tears In My Eyes*?

JULY: Name the duo who reached the Top 5 with the single *Breakin' ... There's No Stoppin' Us.*

AUGUST: Just seven weeks after Lionel Richie saw his original version of *Stuck On You* peak at Number 12, which singer then did a reggae cover of it, reaching Number 9 with that same song?

SEPTEMBER: Which German group sang about being *Big In Japan* on their only Official Singles Chart hit?

OCTOBER: *Together In Electric Dreams* was a Top 3 hit that saw Human League frontman Philip Oakey team up with which acclaimed producer?

NOVEMBER: Limahl reached the Top 5 with theme song to the film *The Neverending Story* – with which band did he score a Number 1 single in 1983?

DECEMBER: Band Aid's *Do They Know It's Christmas* was the biggest-selling song of the eighties – how many weeks did that 1984 original version spend at Number 1 on the Official Singles Chart?

TOP 10: 18 FEBRUARY 1984

Fill in the blanks from this complete Official Singles Chart Top 10. If the song title is listed, we're looking for the band or artist that's missing. If the band or artist is listed, we're looking for the missing song title.

1. (1) FRANKIE GOES TO HOLLYWOOD   ....

2. (2) ....   *RADIO GA GA*

3. (5) ....   *DOCTOR DOCTOR*

4. (3) ....   *GIRLS JUST WANT TO HAVE FUN*

5. (4) MATTHEW WILDER   ....

6. (7) ....   *HOLIDAY*

7. (6) JOE FAGIN   ....

8. (NEW) ....   *MY EVER CHANGING MOODS*

9. (9) ....   *NEW MOON ON MONDAY*

10. (12) JUAN MARTIN   ....

Answers on page 254

All data below refers to positions achieved on the Official Singles Chart or (where relevant) the Official Albums Chart.

JANUARY: Wham! flipped their million-selling double-A -sided single *Last Christmas* and started promoting the other song instead as the lead track – what was its title?

FEBRUARY: Kirsty MacColl reached the Top 10 and scored the biggest solo hit of her entire career with which Billy Bragg song?

MARCH: David Grant and Jaki Graham arrived on the Official Singles Chart with a cover of the 1973 hit *Could It Be I'm Falling In Love?* – name the soul group who had the original Top 20 hit with that song.

APRIL: Who sang the opening line on *We Are The World*, the charity Number 1 hit by USA For Africa?

MAY: *Feel So Real* was the debut hit for which singer?

JUNE: Which group arrived inside the Top 40 with their debut song *Johnny Come Home*?

JULY: Name the 1972 Top 10 solo hit by Michael Jackson which returned to the Official Singles Chart thanks to a charity cover by Marti Webb.

AUGUST: Which singer made their Top 40 debut with the song *Say I'm Your Number One*?

SEPTEMBER: Who claimed to be *Trapped* on his Official Singles Chart Top 40 debut hit?

OCTOBER: Midge Ure had his first solo Number 1 with the song *If I Was*, but with which band did he score a Number 1 in 1976, performing the track *Forever And Ever*?

NOVEMBER: The song *Stairway To Heaven* became a Top 10 hit on the Official Singles Chart for the very first time when it was covered by which studio-based group?

DECEMBER: Name the track that gave Talking Heads their biggest hit and which is still their only song to reach the Top 10.

Answers on page 254

TOP 10: 16 MARCH 1985

Fill in the blanks from this complete Official Singles Chart Top 10. If the song title is listed, we're looking for the band or artist that's missing. If the band or artist is listed, we're looking for the missing song title.

1. (1) DEAD OR ALIVE ....

2. (20) PHILIP BAILEY (DUET WITH PHIL COLLINS) ....

3. (5) .... MATERIAL GIRL

4. (4) STEPHEN 'TIN TIN' DUFFY ....

5. (3) .... NIGHTSHIFT

6. (11) .... THE LAST KISS

7. (18) .... DO WHAT YOU DO

8. (2) ELAINE PAIGE AND BARBARA DICKSON ....

9. (26) .... EVERY TIME YOU GO AWAY

10. (7) .... LET'S GO CRAZY / TAKE ME WITH U

Answers on page 254

All data below refers to positions achieved on the Official Singles Chart or (where relevant) the Official Albums Chart.

JANUARY: Who duetted with Alexander O'Neal on the Top 10 hit *Saturday Love*?

FEBRUARY: What nationality were the duo Double, who scored a Top 10 hit with the song *The Captain Of Her Heart*?

MARCH: Under what alias did musician Prince write *Manic Monday*, a Number 2 hit on the Official Singles Chart for The Bangles?

APRIL: Ten years after reaching Number 1, which song by The Real Thing returned to the Top 10 as a new '86 Decade Remix?

MAY: Marvin Gaye's Motown classic *I Heard It Through he Grapevine* was back inside the Top 10 on re-issue thanks to its use in a famous Levi commercial for their 501 brand – in what year did Marvin reach Number 1 with the song?

JUNE: Valerie Day and John Smith were the husband-and-wife duo Nu Shooz – what was the title of their debut hit which reached Number 2?

JULY: Name the Channel 4 star who teamed up with The Art Of Noise for *Paranoimia*, a song that reached Number 12 on the Official Singles Chart.

AUGUST: What was the title of the only Top 40 hit for the duo Sly Fox?

SEPTEMBER: Peter Cetera scored a Top 3 solo hit with song *Glory Of Love*, but with which band did he score the 1976 Number 1 smash *If You Leave Me Now*?

OCTOBER: *Every Loser Wins* was a Number 1 on the Official Singles Chart for which TV actor?

NOVEMBER: *Through The Barricades* was the last of ten Top 10 hit singles for which group?

DECEMBER: The Housemartins scored their only Number 1 on the Official Singles Chart with a cover of a minor hit from 1985 by Isley/Jasper/Isley – name that song.

Answers on page 254

TOP 10: 23 AUGUST 1986

Fill in the blanks from this complete Official Singles Chart Top 10. If the song title is listed, we're looking for the band or artist that's missing. If the band or artist is listed, we're looking for the missing song title.

1. (2) BORIS GARDINER — ....

2. (1) CHRIS DE BURGH — ....

3. (3) .... — SO MACHO / CRUISING

4. (4) ANITA DOBSON FEATURING THE SIMON MAY ORCHESTRA — ....

5. (5) GWEN GUTHRIE — ....

6. (10) IT BITES — ....

7. (18) .... — DANCING ON THE CEILING

8. (17) .... — I CAN PROVE IT

9. (6) STAN RIDGWAY — ....

10. (8) .... — SHOUT

Answers on page 255

MONTH BY MONTH: 1987

All data below refers to positions achieved on the Official Singles Chart or (where relevant) the Official Albums Chart.

JANUARY: Who made his debut with the Top 10 hit *C'est La Vie*?

FEBRUARY: *It Doesn't Have To Be This Way* was the biggest hit and the only Top 10 song by which band?

MARCH: What was the title of Terence Trent D'Arby's debut hit on the Official Singles Chart?

APRIL: Which two acts teamed up on the Top 10 song *The Irish Rover*?

MAY: The song *Shattered Dreams* was the debut hit on the Official Singles Chart for which trio?

JUNE: The Firm spent a fortnight at Number 1 with which irritating novelty hit?

JULY: Name the group who made their Official Singles Chart debut with *Labour Of Love*?

AUGUST: George Michael provided the uncredited lead vocals on a Top 10 cover version of the 1975 Bee Gees hit *Jive Talkin'* – what name did the group behind this new reworking use for their only chart appearance?

SEPTEMBER: After reaching Number 8 in July with *Sweetest Smile*, which musician matched that same Official Singles Chart peak with his next hit, *Wonderful Life*?

OCTOBER: Two rival versions of the song *I Found Lovin'* both found their way into the Top 10 – one was by The Fatback Band, but who did the other?

NOVEMBER: T'Pau achieved a double by having the Number 1 single on the Official Singles Chart with *China In Your Hand* in the same week that its parent LP topped the Official Albums Chart – what was its three-word title?

DECEMBER: Alison Moyet's cover of the song *Love Letters* peaked at Number 4, matching the 1962 chart position of the version by which American performer?

TOP 10: 28 FEBRUARY 1987

Fill in the blanks from this complete Official Singles Chart Top 10. If the song title is listed, we're looking for the band or artist that's missing. If the band or artist is listed, we're looking for the missing song title.

1. (1) BEN E. KING ....

2. (5) PERCY SLEDGE ....

3. (3) .... DOWN TO EARTH

4. (6) MAN 2 MAN MEETS MAN PARRISH ....

5. (2) .... I KNEW YOU WERE WAITING (FOR ME)

6. (4 .... HEARTACHE

7. (10) .... RUNNING IN THE FAMILY

8. (19) MENTAL AS ANYTHING ....

9. (18) THE JETS ....

10. (14) .... COMING AROUND AGAIN

Answers on page 255

All data below refers to positions achieved on the Official Singles Chart or (where relevant) the Official Albums Chart.

JANUARY: Which 1964 Number 2 hit by The Kinks did The Stranglers take back into the Top 10 on the Official Singles Chart?

FEBRUARY: How many weeks did Kylie Minogue spend at Number 1 with her debut hit *I Should Be So Lucky*?

MARCH: Aswad's Number 1 song *Don't Turn Around* was originally the B-side to a Top 40 hit by Tina Turner in August 1986 – what was the A-side of Tina's single?

APRIL: Which group, fronted by Patsy Kensit, landed their only Top 10 hit with *I'm Not Scared*, a song specially written for them by Neil Tennant and Chris Lowe from Pet Shop Boys?

MAY: Prince had a Top 10 hit single with *Alphabet Street*, taken from his first ever Number 1 on the Official Albums Chart – name that LP.

JUNE: Maxi Priest has a Top 5 hit with the Cat Stevens song *Wild World*, but who first took the song into the Top 10 in September 1970?

JULY: Which 1969 Dusty Springfield album track gave UB40 and Chrissie Hynde a Top 10 hit collaboration on the Official Singles Chart?

AUGUST: Who scored their only Top 10 hit single with their debut *Good Tradition*?

SEPTEMBER: Name the producer who was the featured alongside Inner City on the credits for the Top 10 debut *Big Fun*?

OCTOBER: U2 landed their first-ever Number 1 on the Official Singles Chart with which song?

NOVEMBER: *Need You Tonight* reached Number 2 and became the only Top 10 hit single for which group?

DECEMBER: Which two things went together perfectly, according to the title of the Christmas Number 1 by Cliff Richard?

TOP 10: 5 NOVEMBER 1988

Fill in the blanks from this complete Official Singles Chart Top 10. If the song title is listed, we're looking for the band or artist that's missing. If the band or artist is listed, we're looking for the missing song title.

1. (1) ENYA ....

2. (2) .... *JE NE SAIS PAS POURQUOI*

3. (10) .... *GIRL YOU KNOW IT'S TRUE*

4. (11) .... *STAND UP FOR YOUR LOVE RIGHTS*

5. (19) THE ART OF NOISE FEATURING TOM JONES ....

6. (3) .... *ONE MOMENT IN TIME*

7. (4) D-MOB FEATURING GARY HAISMAN

8. (18) .... *SHE MAKES MY DAY*

9. (7) WEE PAPA GIRL RAPPERS

10. (5) .... *A LITTLE RESPECT*

Answers on page 255

MONTH BY MONTH: 1989

All data below refers to positions achieved on the Official Singles Chart or (where relevant) the Official Albums Chart.

JANUARY: Phil Collins co-wrote, co-produced and played drums on which Top 10 song by The Four Tops?

FEBRUARY: Who did Blow Monkeys frontman Robert Howard team up with on his Official Singles Chart hit *Wait!*?

MARCH: After stalling at Number 52 the previous summer, what one-word title put Sam Brown in the Top 5 following a re-issue?

APRIL: Simply Red spent three weeks at Number 2 with a cover version of *If You Don't Know Me By Now*, but who first had a Top 10 hit with the song in January 1973?

MAY: Which Australian band scored their only Top 40 entry on the Official Singles Chart with *Beds Are Burning*?

JUNE: Name the Italian dance act who took the track *Helyom Halib* into the Top 20.

JULY: *Song For Whoever* was the debut hit and the first of six Top 10 entries on the Official Singles Chart for which group?

AUGUST: *Toy Soldiers* gave Martika her debut hit single – who reinterpreted the track on their February 2005 Number 1 *Like Toy Soldiers*?

SEPTEMBER: The year's biggest-selling single was *Ride On Time* by Black Box – how many weeks did it spend at Number 1 on the Official Singles Chart?

OCTOBER: The song *If Only I Could* spent a fortnight at Number 3 and was the Top 40 debut for which singer?

NOVEMBER: Name the Dutch DJ and producer who took a remix of Jeff Wayne's track *The Eve Of The War* into the Top 3.

DECEMBER: The Stone Roses Top 10 hit *Fools Gold* was officially credited as double-A-sided release with which other song?

TOP 10: 3 JUNE 1989

Fill in the blanks from this complete Official Singles
Chart Top 10. If the song title is listed, we're looking for
the band or artist that's missing. If the band or artist
is listed, we're looking for the missing song title.

1. (1) THE CHRISTIANS, HOLLY JOHNSON, PAUL McCARTNEY, GERRY MARSDEN, AND STOCK AITKEN WATERMAN ....

2. (3) .... *MISS YOU LIKE CRAZY*

3. (13) LYNNE HAMILTON ....

4. (2) .... *HAND ON YOUR HEART*

5. (8) .... *MANCHILD*

6. (4) .... *REQUIEM*

7. (19) .... *I DON'T WANNA GET HURT*

8. (5) EDELWEISS ....

9. (6) .... *EVERY LITTLE STEP*

10. (NEW) .... *EXPRESS YOURSELF*

Answers on page 255-6

ONE-WORD NUMBER 1s

Sometimes just a one-word title is all it takes to send your song flying up to Number 1.

Here are 40 fine examples from right across the first 70 years of the Official Singles Chart.

Who sang these hits?

1.   *Geno* [May 1980]

2.   *Bulletproof* [July 2009]

3.   *Freedom* [October 1984]

4.   *Smile* [July 2006]

5.   *Once* [May 2010]

6.   *If* [March 1975]

7.   *Babe* [December 1993]

8.   *Shivers* [September 2021]

9.   *Louder* [July 2011]

10. *Dare* [September 2005]

11. *Imagine* [January 1981]

12. *Free* [May 1977]

13. *King* [March 2015]

14. *Bonkers* [May 2009]

15. *Animals* [November 2013]

16. *Positions* [November 2020]

17. *Dreamer* [May 1995]

18. *Dilemma* [October 2002]

19. *Crying* [June 1980]

20. *Tears* [September 1965]

21. *Stay* [February 1992]

22. *Beautiful* [March 2003]

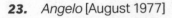

23. *Angelo* [August 1977]

24. *Relax* [January 1984]

25. *Replay* [January 2010]

26. *Dakota* [March 2005]

27. *She* [June 1974]

28. *Blame* [September 2014]

29. *Vertigo* [November 2004]

30. *Rise* [February 2000]

31. *Start* [September 1980]

32. *Cars* [September 1979]

33. *Lemonade* [October 2020]

34. *Titanium* [February 2012]

35. *Radio* [October 2004]

36. *Symphony* [May 2017]

37. *Flava* [September 1996]

38. *Sailor* [February 1961]

39. *Mississippi* [October 1976]

40. *Music* [September 2000]

Answers on page 256

CALLING YOUR NAME

Not only did that title give Marilyn their Official Singles Chart debut and take them all the way to Number 4 in December 1983, but it also seemed like a rather appropriate heading for a section featuring a bunch of other popstars who just needed one name to become famous.

See if you can correctly identify all 20 individuals who brought us these great songs.

1. *It's Oh So Quiet* [Number 4 in December 1995]

2. *Rolling In The Deep* [Number 2 in January 2011]

3. *Kiss From A Rose* [Number 4 in August 1995]

4. *Causing A Commotion* [Number 4 in September 1987]

5. *Who's That Girl?* [Number 6 in May 2001]

6. *If I Ever Lose My Faith In You* [Number 14 in February 1993]

7. *White Flag* [Number 2 in September 2003]

8. *I Love Your Smile* [Number 2 in March 1992]

9. *Mellow Yellow* [Number 8 in March 1967]

10. *Show Me Love* [Number 8 in March 1998]

11. *Cheap Thrills* [Number 2 in April 2016]

12. *Lonely* [Number 1 in May 2005]

13. *Book Of Days* [Number 10 in August 1992]

14. *Pop Ya Collar* [Number 2 in February 2001]

15. *Love... Thy Will Be Done* [Number 9 in September 1991]

16. *Porcelain* [Number 5 in June 2000]

17. *Don't Call Me Up* [Number 3 in March 2019]

18. *Underneath Your Clothes* [Number 3 in August 2002]

19. *Devils Haircut* [Number 22 in November 1996]

20. *More Than A Woman* [Number 1 in January 2002]

Answers on page 256

NOW THAT'S WHAT I CALL AN OPENER

Below are the opening songs on 20 of the first 100
NOW That's What I Call Music! albums. We'll give you the
volume number and year of its release, as well as the band
or artist who had the honour of being the lead track.

Can you identify the correct titles, all of which also
went to Number 1 on the Official Singles Chart?

1. **NOW 13** [1988]: Yazz & The Plastic Population

2. **NOW 29** [1994]: Pato Banton with Ali & Robin Campbell

3. **NOW 9** [1987]: Jackie Wilson

4. **NOW 52** [2002]: Ronan Keating

5. **NOW 11** [1988] Pet Shop Boys

6. **NOW 99** [2018] Camila Cabello featuring Young Thug

7. **NOW 78** [2011]: Bruno Mars

8. **NOW 1** [1983]: Phil Collins

9. **NOW 81** [2012]: Gotye featuring Kimbra

10. **NOW 45** [2000]: Gabrielle

11. **NOW 25** [1993]: George Michael and Queen

12. **NOW 3** [1984]: Duran Duran

13. **NOW 71** [2008]: Girls Aloud

14. **NOW 34** [1996]: Spice Girls

15. **NOW 23** [1992]: Tasmin Archer

16. **NOW 12** [1988]: Wet Wet Wet

17. **NOW 88** [2014]: Ella Henderson

18. **NOW 62** [2005]: Sugababes

19. **NOW 57** [2004]: Britney Spears

20. **NOW 79** [2011]: Adele

Answers on page 256-7

YOU'RE SPEAKING MY LANGUAGE

We suspect only true Official Singles Chart geeks will be aware that the title we've given to this next selection of songs was also a Number 35 debut for Juliette & The Licks in May 2005.

Give yourself a very large pat on the back if you knew that, and then try to figure out who turned these non-English language titles into successful UK hits.

1. *La Bamba* [Number 1 in August 1987]

2. *Encore Une Fois* [Number 2 in February 1997]

3. *Chanson D'Amour* [Number 1 in March 1977]

4. *Autobahn* [Number 11 in June 1975]

5. *Pie Jesu* [Number 3 in March 1985]

6. *Comment Te Dire Adieu* [Number 14 in November 1989]

7. *Im Nin'alu* [Number 15 in May 1988]

8. *Pour Que Tu M'aimes Encore* [Number 7 in September 1995]

9. *Dragostea Din Tei* [Number 3 in June 2004]

10. *Y Viva Espana* [Number 4 in September 1974]

11. *Moi ... Lolita* [Number 9 in February 2002]

12. *Je T'aime ... Moi Non Plus* [Number 1 in October 1969]

13. *Mundian To Bach Ke* [Number 5 in January 2003]

14. *Gaudete* [Number 14 in December 1973]

15. *Yé ké yé ké* [Number 29 in August 1988]

16. *Ca Plane Pour Moi* [Number 8 in June 1978]

17. *Guantanamera* [Number 7 in October 1966]

18. *Nessun Dorma* [Number 2 in June 1990]

19. *Dominique* [Number 7 in December 1963]

20. *Mas Que Nada* [Number 6 in June 2006]

HIT AFTER HIT:
BILLY OCEAN

Place these five **BILLY OCEAN** hits in their
correct chronological order as they each
appeared on the Official Singles Chart.

A. *LOVERBOY*

B. *THERE'LL BE SAD SONGS (TO MAKE YOU CRY)*

C. *SUDDENLY*

D. *GET OUTTA MY DREAMS, GET INTO MY CAR*

E. *RED LIGHT SPELLS DANGER*

Answers on page 257

ONE TO FIVE:
TOM JONES

Each of these **TOM JONES** hits achieved a different
peak position on the Official Singles Chart – put
them in the correct order, starting with Number 1
and working your way down to Number 5.

A. *SEX BOMB (WITH MOUSSE T)*

B. *HELP YOURSELF*

C. *MAMA TOLD ME NOT TO COME (WITH STEREOPHONICS)*

D. *GREEN GREEN GRASS OF HOME*

E. *DELILAH*

Answers on page 257

HIT AFTER HIT:
UB40

Place these eighties hits by **UB40** in their correct chronological order as they appeared on the Official Singles Chart during that decade.

A. RED RED WINE

B. FOOD FOR THOUGHT

C. ONE IN TEN

D. RAT IN MI KITCHEN

E. IF IT HAPPENS AGAIN

Answers on page 257

ONE TO FIVE:
THE STYLISTICS

Each of these hits by **THE STYLISTICS** achieved a different peak position on the Official Singles Chart – put them in the correct order, starting with Number 1 and working your way down to Number 5.

A. CAN'T HELP FALLING IN LOVE

B. CAN'T GIVE YOU ANYTHING (BUT MY LOVE)

C. SING BABY SING

D. NA NA IS THE SADDEST WORD

E. YOU MAKE ME FEEL BRAND NEW

Answers on page 257

NAME AND NUMBER

Each of the following 20 acts all have a number in their name.

We've given you the title of one of their biggest songs on the Official Singles Chart, along with its peak position and year.

All you need to do is correctly identify who they are.

1. *Love Shack* [Number 2 in March 1990]

2. *In Da Club* [Number 3 in April 2003]

3. *Bring It All Back* [Number 1 in June 1999]

4. *Kingston Town* [Number 4 in April 1990]

5. *I Miss You* [Number 8 on March 2004]

6. *Concrete And Clay* [Number 1 in April 1965]

7. *Baby Cakes* [Number 1 in August 2004]

8. *Hot Water* [Number 18 in September 1984]

9. *The Sound* [Number 15 in January 2016]

10. *Ain't Talkin' 'Bout Dub* [Number 7 in February 1997]

11. *Touch Me* [Number 3 in January 1990]

12. *Fat Lip* [Number 8 in October 2001]

13. *She Looks So Perfect* [Number 1 in April 2014]

14. *Café Del Mar '98* [Number 12 in July 1998]

15. *Hurry Up Harry* [Number 10 in November 1978]

16. *Crushed By The Wheels Of Industry* [Number 17 in September 1983]

17. *Come Baby Come* [Number 3 in January 1994]

18. *Activ 8 (Come With Me)* [Number 3 in November 1991]

19. *Bohemian Rhapsody* [Number 9 in March 2005]

20. *I Still Haven't Found What I'm Looking For* [Number 6 in June 1987]

Answers on page 257

SUPERSTAR SPOTLIGHT:
KATE BUSH

1. How many years were there between Kate's first Official Singles Chart Number 1, *Wuthering Heights*, and her second, *Running Up That Hill*?

2. Peter Gabriel collaborated with Kate in 1986 on which Official Top 10 hit single?

3. In 1980, Kate scored her first Official Albums Chart Number 1 – what was the title of that album?

4. With which Elton John song did Kate score a Top 20 hit just before Christmas 1991?

5. Between 2000 and 2010, Kate achieved just one Official UK Top 40 entry – what was its title?

6. Place these five Kate Bush hits in their correct chronological order as they each appeared on the Official Singles Chart.

   a. *Babooshka*
   b. *The Sensual World*
   c. *Sat In Your Lap*
   d. *The Man With The Child In His Eyes*
   e. *Cloudbusting*

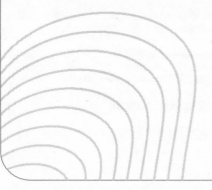

Answers on page 257

WHO'S DAVID?

That's the question that Busted posed on their Number 1 hit in February 2004, and we thought we'd ask it again now.

Every one of these 20 songs was made famous by a fella called Dave or David when it appeared on the Official Singles Chart.

How many do you know?

1.   *Don't Give Up On Us* [Number 1 in January 1977]

2.   *Babylon* [Number 5 in June 2000]

3.   *The Laughing Gnome* [Number 6 in October 1973]

4.   *Starlight* [Number 1 in March 2022]

5.   *Gonna Make You A Star* [Number 1 in November 1974]

6.   *Santo Natale* [Number 2 in December 1954]

7.   *How Can I Be Sure?* [Number 1 in September 1972]

8.   *The Crying Game* [Number 5 in September 1964]

9.   *You Can't Hide (Your Love From Me)* [Number 13 in March 1983]

10.   *Walk Away From Love* [Number 10 in February 1976]

11.   *House Every Weekend* [Number 1 in July 2015]

12.   *Isn't She Lovely?* [Number 4 in January 1977]

13.   *Just Like Paradise* [Number 27 in March 1988]

14.   *Stop Living The Lie* [Number 1 in January 2003]

15.   *Girls Talk* [Number 4 in July 1979]

16.   *Watching You Watching Me* [Number 10 in September 1983]

17.   *Death Of A Clown* [Number 3 in August 1967]

18.   *Red Guitar* [Number 17 in June 1984]

19.   *Jeans On* [Number 3 in August 1976]

20.   *Take Five* [Number 6 in November 1961]

Answers on page 257-8

SAME TITLE, DIFFERENT SONGS

Throughout the first 70 years of the Official Singles Chart, many bands and artists have shared the same song titles, but both with completely different tunes.

How many hits can you name from this list?

1. Lionel Richie [1984] / Adele [2015]

2. Wham! [1984] / Robbie Williams [1996]

3. Stevie Wonder [1981] / Altered Images [1981]

4. Fairground Attraction [1988] / Ed Sheeran [2017]

5. Little Mix [2012] / Birdy [2013]

6. The Human League [1981] / M People [1995]

7. Simple Minds [1986] / t.a.T.u [2003]

8. Level 42 [1995] / Jamelia [2006]

9. Leona Lewis [2009] / Pharrell Williams [2013]

10. Coldplay [2011] / George Ezra [2018]

11. Seal [1990] / Gnarls Barkley [2006]

12. Chic [1979] / Atomic Kitten [2000]

13. Madonna [1985] / Let Loose [1994]

14. Roy Orbison [1963] / Julee Cruise [1990]

15. Nick Berry [1992] / Steps [1998]

16. Alison Moyet [1986] / Whitesnake [1987]

17. Kiki Dee [1981] / Erasure [1990]

18. Daryl Hall & John Oates [1982] / Nelly Furtado [2006]

19. Brothers Johnson [1980] / Steps [2000]

20. Gilbert O'Sullivan [1973] / Gene Chandler [1979]

21. Madonna [1985] / Shaggy featuring Rayvon [2000]

22. Ozzy & Kelly Osbourne [2003] / FAUL & Wad Ad vs Pnau [2014]

23. En Vogue [1990] / Wilson Phillips [1990]

24. Swing Out Sister [1986] / Foo Fighters [2000]

25. Shakespears Sister [1992] / Rihanna featuring Mikky Ekko [2012]

26. Sally Oldfield [1978] / Justin Timberlake [2013]

27. The Ronettes [1963] / Vanessa Paradis [1992]

28. Nickelback [2007] / Post Malone featuring 21 Savage [2017]

29. Del Shannon [1961] / The Corrs [1999]

30. ABBA [1978] / JLS [2011]

31. Yarbrough And Peoples [1981] / Rihanna [2007]

32. Livin' Joy [1996] / S Club 7 [2001]

33. Kim Appleby [1990] / Appleton [2003]

34. Lisa Stansfield [1989] / Oasis [1998]

35. Haddaway [1995] / Lenny Kravitz [1999]

36. Free [1973] / Terence Trent D'Arby [1987]

37. Nirvana [1992] / Beverley Knight [2004]

38. PhD [1982] / James Morrison [2011]

39. Rockers Revenge featuring Donnie Calvin [1982] / Katrina And The Waves [1985]

40. Blancmange [1983] / Mr. Probz [2014]

Answers on page 258

HIT AFTER HIT:
ROBBIE WILLIAMS

Place these five **ROBBIE WILLIAMS** solo hits in their correct chronological order as they each appeared on the Official Singles Chart

A. SHE'S THE ONE

B. OLD BEFORE I DIE

C. ROCK DJ

D. FEEL

E. RUDEBOX

Answers on page 258

ONE TO FIVE:
FRANK SINATRA

Each of these **FRANK SINATRA** hits achieved a different peak position on the Official Singles Chart – put them in the correct order, starting with Number 1 and working your way down to Number 5.

A. LOVE AND MARRIAGE

B. (LOVE IS) THE TENDER TRAP

C. THEME FROM 'NEW YORK, NEW YORK'

D. STRANGERS IN THE NIGHT

E. MY WAY

Answers on page 258

I KNOW WHAT I LIKE (IN YOUR WARDROBE)

So said Genesis in April 1974 on their Top 20 hit, but can you name the various bands and artists who mentioned items of clothing and assorted garments in these song titles that have all appeared on the Official Singles Chart from the seventies onwards?

1. *Baggy Trousers* [Number 3 in October 1980]

2. *Itsy Bitsy Teeny Weeny Yellow Polka Dot Bikini* [Number 1 in August 1990]

3. *Crocodile Shoes* [Number 4 in December 1994]

4. *Same Jeans* [Number 3 in January 2007]

5. *Handbags & Gladrags* [Number 4 in December 2001]

6. *Suit And Tie* [Number 3 in January 2013]

7. *Raspberry Beret* [Number 25 in August 1985]

8. *T-Shirt* [Number 6 in February 2009]

9. *Favourite Shirts (Boy Meets Girl)* [Number 4 in November 1981]

10. *Fancy Pants* [Number 4 in April 1975]

11. *The Ladies' Bras* [Number 27 in October 2007]

12. *Thong Song* [Number 3 in April 2000]

13. *Pyjamarama* [Number 10 in April 1973]

14. *Cardigan* [Number 6 in August 2020]

15. *Kinky Boots* [Number 5 in December 1990]

16. *Leap Up And Down (Wave Your Knickers In The Air)* [Number 12 in July 1971]

17. *Hand In Glove* [Number 27 in May 1984]

18. *Silver Shorts* [Number 14 in April 1992]

19. *Wherever I Lay My Hat (That's My Home)* [Number 1 in July 1983]

20. *Red Dress* [Number 4 in March 2006]

Answers on page 258

SUPERSTAR SPOTLIGHT:
ABBA

1. In what year did ABBA win the Eurovision Song Contest in Brighton and then make their Official Singles Chart debut shortly afterwards with *Waterloo*?

2. Since then, how many UK Number 1 singles has the band scored?

3. Agnetha Fältskog's 2004 solo single *If I Thought You'd Ever Change Your Mind* reached Number 11 and was a cover of a Top 20 hit from January 1970 by which British singer?

4. ABBA's *Gold – Greatest Hits* collection was first released in the autumn of 1992 and is now the second-biggest seller of all time in the UK – how many weeks in total has it spent at Number 1 on the Official Albums Chart?

5. The first time Benny and Björn officially approved any of their music to be sampled by another act was for the 1997 Fugees hit *Rumble In The Jungle* – which of ABBA's Number 1 songs from the seventies was used on that track?

6. Place these seventies hits by ABBA in their correct chronological order as they each appeared on the Official Singles Chart during that decade.

    a. *Fernando*
    b. *S.O.S.*
    c. *Chiquitita*
    d. *Knowing Me, Knowing You*
    e. *Money, Money, Money*

Answers on page 259

HIT AFTER HIT:
GENESIS

Place these eighties hits by **GENESIS** in their correct chronological order as they appeared on the Official Singles Chart during that decade.

A. THAT'S ALL

B. TURN IT ON AGAIN

C. MAMA

D. LAND OF CONFUSION

E. ABACAB

Answers on page 259

ONE TO FIVE:
U2

Each of these **U2** hits achieved a different peak position on the Official Singles Chart – put them in the correct order, starting with Number 1 and working your way down to Number 5.

A. BEAUTIFUL DAY

B. SWEETEST THING

C. WITH OR WITHOUT YOU

D. ELECTRICAL STORM

E. HOLD ME, THRILL ME, KISS ME, KILL ME

Answers on page 259

MISSING WORDS

In this selection of songs, we've removed all the words that were originally listed in brackets when each of these titles appeared on the Top 20 during the eighties. We've listed each band or artist along with their peak chart position and year, so all you've got to do now is fill in the blanks.

Oh, and you should give yourself an extra bonus point if you spotted that the title of this section was also the name of The Selecter's third Top 40 hit on the Official Singles Chart, back in 1980!

1.   *Chant No.1 (___ ___ ___ ___ ___ ___)*
     Spandau Ballet [Number 3 in August 1981]

2.   *Back To Life (___ ___ ___ ___ ___)*
     Soul II Soul featuring Caron Wheeler [Number 1 in June 1989]

3.   *Love Action (___ ___ ___ ___)*
     The Human League [Number 3 in August 1981]

4.   *(___ ___) Starting Over*
     John Lennon [Number 1 in December 1980]

5.   *Oh Patti (___ ___ ___ ___ ___)*
     Scritti Politti [Number 13 in June 1988]

6.   *Arthur's Theme (___ ___ ___ ___ ___)*
     Christopher Cross [Number 7 in February 1982]

7.   *All Night Long (___ ___)*
     Lionel Richie [Number 2 in October 1983]

8.   *Pride (___ ___ ___ ___ ___)*
     U2 [Number 3 in September 1984]

9.   *Hands Up (___ ___ ___ ___)*
     Ottawan [Number 3 in September 1981]

10. *I Wanna Dance With Somebody (___ ___ ___)*
     Whitney Houston [Number 1 in June 1987]

11. *Time (___ ___ ___ ___)*
     Culture Club [Number 3 in December 1982]

12. *The Sun Goes Down (___ ___ ___)*
     Level 42 [Number 10 in September 1983]

13. *New Beginning (___ ___)*
Bucks Fizz [Number 8 in June 1986]

14. *Don't You (___ ___ ___)*
Simple Minds [Number 7 in May 1985]

15. *Superman (___ ___)*
Black Lace [Number 9 in October 1983]

16. *St. Elmo's Fire (___ ___ ___)*
John Parr [Number 6 in October 1985]

17. *(___ ___) Died In Your Arms*
Cutting Crew [Number 4 in September 1986]

18. *Showing Out (___ ___ ___ ___ ___)*
Mel & Kim [Number 3 in November 1986]

19. *Lean On Me (___ ___ ___)*
Red Box [Number 3 in October 1985]

20. *Young Guns (___ ___ ___)*
Wham! [Number 3 in December 1982]

21. *Dancing On The Floor (___ ___ ___)*
Third World [Number 10 in July 1981]

22. *Whatever I Do (___ ___ ___ ___)*
Hazell Dean [Number 4 in August 1984]

23. *Real Wild Child (___ ___)*
    Iggy Pop [Number 10 in January 1987]

24. *Against All Odds (___ ___ ___ ___ ___ ___)*
    Phil Collins [Number 2 in April 1984]

25. *White Lines (___ ___ ___ ___)*
    Grandmaster And Melle Mel [Number 7 in July 1984]

26. *Jump (___ ___ ___)*
    The Pointer Sisters [Number 6 in June 1984]

27. *You Spin Me Round (___ ___ ___)*
    Dead Or Alive [Number 1 in March 1985]

28. *(___ ___) Just Buggin'*
    Whistle [Number 7 in March 1986]

29. *I'm Gonna Be (___ ___)*
    The Proclaimers [Number 11 in October 1988]

30. *Opportunities (___ ___ ___ ___ ___)*
    Pet Shop Boys [Number 11 in June 1986]

31. *(___ ___) So Strong*
    Labi Siffre [Number 4 in May 1987]

32. *We Take Mystery (___ ___)*
    Gary Numan [Number 9 in June 1982]

33. *(___ ___) Heaven*
    Fiction Factory [Number 6 in February 1984]

34. *I Can't Go For That (__ __ __)*
Daryl Hall & John Oates [Number 8 in February 1982]

35. *Wishing (__ __ __ __ __ __ __)*
A Flock Of Seagulls [Number 10 in December 1982]

36. *Loadsamoney (__ __ __ __)*
Harry Enfield [Number 4 in May 1988]

37. *Fields Of Fire (__ __)*
Big Country [Number 10 in April 1983]

38. *Sad Songs (__ __ __)*
Elton John [Number 7 in June 1984]

39. *Caribbean Queen (__ __ __ __ __ __)*
Billy Ocean [Number 6 in November 1984]

40. *Burning Bridges (__ __ __ __ __ __)*
Status Quo [Number 5 in December 1988]

Answers on page 259

HIT AFTER HIT:
A-HA

Place these eighties hits by **A-HA** in their correct chronological order as they appeared on the Official Singles Chart during that decade.

A. CRY WOLF

B. HUNTING HIGH AND LOW

C. TAKE ON ME

D. THE LIVING DAYLIGHTS

E. THE SUN ALWAYS SHINES ON TV

Answers on page 259

ONE TO FIVE:
EURYTHMICS

Each of these **EURYTHMICS** hits achieved a different peak position on the Official Singles Chart – put them in the correct order, starting with Number 1 and working your way down to Number 5.

A. SWEET DREAMS (ARE MADE OF THIS)

B. THORN IN MY SIDE

C. THERE MUST BE AN ANGEL (PLAYING WITH MY HEART)

D. WHO'S THAT GIRL

E. SEXCRIME (NINETEEN EIGHTY-FOUR)

Answers on page 259

GET A LIFE

So said Soul II Soul on one of the great Top 10 hits back in December 1989.

It set us off rummaging around the Official Singles Chart archive to find 20 other life-themed songs.

Just name the bands and artists behind these tunes.

1. *For Once In My Life* [Number 3 in January 1969]

2. *Don't Give Me Your Life* [Number 2 in March 1995]

3. *My Life* [Number 12 in February 1979]

4. *Good Life* [Number 4 in January 1989]

5. *My Life Would Suck Without You* [Number 1 in March 2009]

6. *Ain't Got No: I Got Life* [Number 2 in December 1968]

7. *Come Into My Life* [Number 7 in January 1988]

8. *Ooh! What A Life* [Number 10 in September 1979]

9. *If You Buy This Record Your Life Will Be Better* [Number 3 in November 1998]

10. *Life's Been Good* [Number 14 in August 1978]

11. *Got To Get You Into My Life* [Number 6 in September 1966]

12. *It's My Life* [Number 2 in September 1992]

13. *The Story Of My Life* [Number 1 in February 1958]

14. *How To Save A Life* [Number 4 in April 2007]

15. *Live Is Life* [Number 6 in August 1985]

16. *Reflections Of My Life* [Number 3 in January 1970]

17. *Key To My Life* [Number 3 in May 1995]

18. *18 And Life* [Number 12 in February 1990]

19. *Last Night A DJ Saved My Life* [Number 13 in February 1983]

20. *Bring Me To Life* [Number 1 in June 2003]

Answers on page 259

SCOTLAND FOREVER

Musicians from Scotland have consistently graced the Official Singles Chart during its first 70 years and continue to do so. We celebrate the range of sounds and styles here with 20 titles.

Do you know the names of the proud Scots who made them?

1.   *No More 'I Love You's* [Number 2 in February 1995]

2.   *Letter From America* [Number 3 in December 1987]

3.   *Next To Me* [Number 2 in February 2012]

4.   *Looking For Linda* [Number 15 in March 1989]

5.   *Oblivious* [Number 18 in December 1983]

6.   *Suddenly I See* [Number 12 in September 2005]

7.   *April Skies* [Number 8 in May 1987]

8.   *Year Of The Cat* [Number 31 in February 1977]

9.   *Don't Talk To Me About Love* [Number 7 in March 1983]

10. *Driftwood* [Number 13 in May 1999]

11. *Since Yesterday* [Number 5 in January 1985]

12. *A Girl Like You* [Number 4 in July 1995]

13. *Night Owl* [Number 5 in July 1979]

14. *I'm Falling* [Number 11 in May 1984]

15. *To Love Somebody* [Number 8 in November 1990]

16. *The Honeythief* [Number 17 in March 1986]

17. *January February* [Number 11 in April 1980]

18. *Big Wedge* [Number 25 in January 1990]

19. *Ab Ubhal As Airde (The Highest Apple)* [Number 18 in May 1995]

20. *For Your Eyes Only* [Number 8 in August 1981]

GIRLS, GIRLS, GIRLS

All it took was just a single girl's name and nothing else to put these 20 performers and groups into the Official Singles Chart.

Now see if you can figure out the singers and musicians who had these hits.

1.   *Delilah* [Number 2 in March 1968]

2.   *Ruby* [Number 1 in March 2007]

3.   *Angie* [Number 5 in September 1973]

4.   *Joanna* [Number 2 in March 1984]

5.   *Eloise* [Number 2 in November 1968]

6.   *Carrie* [Number 4 in March 1980]

7.   *Mary* [Number 14 in October 2004]

8.   *Gloria* [Number 6 in February 1983]

9.   *Clair* [Number 1 in November 1972]

10. *Emma* [Number 3 in April 1974]

11. *Rosanna* [Number 12 in April 1983]

12. *Sandy* [Number 2 in November 1978]

13. *Louise* [Number 13 in December 1984]

14. *Juliet* [Number 1 in May 1964]

15. *Sarah* [Number 24 in December 1979]

16. *Kayleigh* [Number 2 in June 1985]

17. *Sylvia* [Number 4 in February 1973]

18. *Susanna* [Number 12 in June 1984]

19. *Valerie* [Number 2 in October 2007]

20. *Maria* [Number 1 in February 1999]

Answers on page 260

2 BECOME 1

Here are 20 songs that brought together two established bands or solo stars to create a Number 1 single on the Official Singles Chart.

Name **BOTH** acts who were credited on each of these titles.

1. *I Knew You Were Waiting (For Me)* [February 1987]

2. *Hips Don't Lie* [July 2006]

3. *Relight My Fire* [October 1993]

4. *Xanadu* [July 1980]

5. *Number 1* [May 2009]

6. *Telephone* [March 2010]

7. *Walk This Way* [March 2007]

8. *Ebony And Ivory* [April 1982]

9. *Heart Skips A Beat* [September 2011]

10. *Dizzy* [November 1991]

11. *Lay Me Down* [March 2015]

12. *Especially For You* [January 1989]

13. *We Found Love* [October 2011]

14. *American Boy* [March 2008]

15. *Sorry Seems To Be The Hardest Word* [2002]

16. *I Know Him So Well* [February 1985]

17. *4 Minutes* [April 2008]

18. *The Long And Winding Road* [October 2002]

19. *R.I.P.* [May 2012]

20. *Against All Odds* [September 2000]

SUPERSTAR SPOTLIGHT:
GEORGE MICHAEL

1. Wham! only ever released two studio albums, both of which went to Number 1 on the Official Albums Chart – the first was titled *Fantastic*, but what was the second?

2. Which four words complete the title of Wham!'s second Top 10 hit, *Wham Rap! (___ ___ ___ ___)?*

3. How many weeks did the song *Careless Whisper* spend at Number 1 on the Official Singles Chart in 1984?

4. Name Wham's! farewell song, which went to Number 1 just before George and Andrew split in June 1986.

5. Which Stevie Wonder song did George cover in 1999 in collaboration with Mary J. Blige and take into the Top 5 on the Official Singles Chart?

6. Place these five nineties hits by George in their correct chronological order as they each appeared on the Official Singles Chart during the decade.

    a. *Praying For Time*
    b. *Outside*
    c. *Jesus To A Child*
    d. *Fastlove*
    e. *Too Funky*

Answers on page 260

WHAT'S MY NAME?

Robyn Rihanna Fenty (just plain Rihanna to you and me) teamed up with Aubrey Drake Graham (yes, that's Drake) for the 2011 Number 1 song that inspired this next set of questions.

All these popstars appeared on big hits during the first 70 years of the Official Singles Chart but used an alias or stage name to get famous.

How many can you identify?

1. Farrokh Bulsara

2. Stefani Joanne Angelina Germanotta

3. Harry Rodger Webb

4. Shawn Corey Carter

5. Adam Richard Wiles

6. Yvette Marie Stephens

7. Stanley Kirk Burrell

8. Pauline Matthews

9. Curtis James Jackson III

10. Declan Patrick Aloysius MacManus

11. Michael Ebenezer Kwadjo Omari Owuo Jr

12. Cherilyn Sarkisian

13. Armando Christian Pérez

14. Melissa Viviane Jefferson

15. Peter Gene Hernandez

16. Marshall Bruce Mathers III

17. Ella Marija Lani Yelich-O'Connor

18. Abel Makkonen Tesfaye

19. Orville Richard Burrell

20. Calvin Cordozar Broadus Jr

Answers on page 260-1

HIT AFTER HIT:
ERASURE

Place these nineties hits by **ERASURE** in their correct chronological order as they appeared on the Official Singles Chart during that decade.

A. LOVE TO HATE YOU

B. BLUE SAVANNAH

C. BREATH OF LIFE

D. CHORUS

E. ALWAYS

Answers on page 261

ONE TO FIVE:
JASON DERULO

Each of these **JASON DERULO** hits achieved a different peak position on the Official Singles Chart – put them in the correct order, starting with Number 1 and working your way down to Number 5.

A. TRUMPETS

B. RIDIN' SOLO

C. WANT TO WANT ME

D. TIP TOE (FEATURING FRENCH MONTANA)

E. WHATCHA SAY

Answers on page 261

NUL POINTS

The UK's success at Eurovision took an unexpected turn in 2022 when we were runners-up in Turin, and 2023 will always be known as the year the contest took place on home soil for the first time in 25 years.

Here are 20 of the UK's entries from the sixties to the noughties, all of which reached the Top 20 on the Official Singles Chart.

Who performed them?

1. *Puppet On A String* [Number 1 in April 1967]

2. *Flying The Flag For You* [Number 5 in May 2007]

3. *Boom Bang-A-Bang* [Number 2 in April 1969]

4. *Cry Baby* [Number 15 in June 2003]

5. *One Step Further* [Number 2 in May 1982]

6. *Rock Bottom* [Number 19 in April 1977]

7. *Where Are You?* [Number 15 in May 1998]

8. *Touch My Fire* [Number 18 in May 2005]

9. *Long Live Love* [Number 11 in April 1974]

10. *Love Games* [Number 11 in 1984]

11. *Say Wonderful Things* [Number 6 in April 1963]

12. *Jack In The Box* [Number 4 in April 1971]

13. *Teenage Life* [Number 8 in June 2006]

14. *Let Me Be The One* [Number 12 in April 1975]

15. *I Can* [Number 16 in May 2011]

16. *Are You Sure?* [Number 2 in March 1961]

17. *Come Back* [Number 13 in 2002]

18. *Better The Devil You Know* [Number 15 in May 1993]

19. *Bad Old Days* [Number 13 in May 1978]

20. *One Step Out Of Time* [Number 20 in April 1992]

Answers on page 261

HIT AFTER HIT:
BLONDIE

Place these five **BLONDIE** hits in their correct chronological order as they each appeared on the Official Singles Chart.

- **A.** THE TIDE IS HIGH
- **B.** DENIS
- **C.** PICTURE THIS
- **D.** CALL ME
- **E.** RAPTURE

Answers on page 261

ONE TO FIVE:
ADAM AND THE ANTS

Each of these **ADAM AND THE ANTS** hits achieved a different peak position on the Official Singles Chart – put them in the correct order, starting with Number 1 and working your way down to Number 5.

- **A.** ANTMUSIC
- **B.** PUSS 'N BOOTS (*ADAM ANT SOLO)
- **C.** DOG EAT DOG
- **D.** ANT RAP
- **E.** STAND AND DELIVER

Answers on page 261

SPOTLIGHT:
1990s

MONTH BY MONTH: 1990

All data below refers to positions achieved on the Official Singles Chart or (where relevant) the Official Albums Chart.

JANUARY: Which singer covered Sylvester's 1978 Top 10 hit *You Make Me Feel (Mighty Real)* and took it even higher on the Official Singles Chart than the original version?

FEBRUARY: Which 1964 Top 10 hit by Dionne Warwick was covered by The Stranglers in 1978, but reached its best-ever position on the Top 40 thanks to the version performed by Sybil?

MARCH: Name the Canadian musician who made her Official Singles Chart debut with the song *Black Velvet*.

APRIL: Candy Flip were in the Top 3 with a cover of *Strawberry Fields Forever* – which other song featured on the double-A-sided single when The Beatles first took the track to Number 2 in 1967?

MAY: The Top 10 hit *Ghetto Heaven* was the only song that ever made it onto the Official Singles Chart for which group?

JUNE: Don Pablo's Animals reached Number 4 with the most successful UK hit version of a song that Bananarama covered in 1986 – name it.

JULY: *The Great Song Of Indifference* was the biggest solo hit single for which Irish musician?

AUGUST: Go West's song *The King Of Wishful Thinking* was a Top 20 hit and featured on the soundtrack album for one of 1990's biggest romcoms – what was the movie?

SEPTEMBER: Deacon Blue spent a fortnight at Number 2 with their *Four Bacharach & David Songs* EP – the lead track was a cover of which 1969 Bobbie Gentry Number 1?

OCTOBER: After featuring on a TV ad for Nivea face cream, which 1963 Bobby Vinton song suddenly appeared inside the Top 20 for the very first time?

NOVEMBER: *Don't Worry* put which singer inside the Top 10 for the first time as a solo star?

DECEMBER: The soundtrack to the Nicolas Cage film *Wild At Heart* provided Chris Isaak with his only Top 10 hit single – what was the song title?

TOP 10: 4 AUGUST 1990

Fill in the blanks from this complete Official Singles Chart Top 10. If the song title is listed, we're looking for the band or artist that's missing. If the band or artist is listed, we're looking for the missing song title.

1. (1) PARTNERS IN KRYME ....

2. (4) .... *HANKY PANKY*

3. (13) DNA FEATURING SUZANNE VEGA ....

4. (2) .... *SACRIFICE / HEALING HANDS*

5. (5) .... *U CAN'T TOUCH THIS*

6. (8) BLUE PEARL ....

7. (3) CRAIG McLACHLAN & CHECK 1-2 ....

8. (10) THE SOUP DRAGONS FEATURING JUNIOR REID ....

9. (9) .... *ROCKIN' OVER THE BEAT*

10. (7) .... *IT MUST HAVE BEEN LOVE*

Answers on page 261

MONTH BY MONTH: 1991

All data below refers to positions achieved on the Official Singles Chart or (where relevant) the Official Albums Chart.

JANUARY: The song *International Bright Young Thing* was the first Top 10 hit single for which band?

FEBRUARY: Identical twin sisters Jacqui and Pauline Cuff were the duo Soho – which 1985 song by The Smiths did they sample on their Top 10 hit *Hippychick*?

MARCH: Production duo Quartz reached the Top 10 with a cover of Carole King's song *It's Too Late* – who made her Official Singles Chart debut as the featured vocalist on the Quartz track?

APRIL: After being absent from the Top 40 since 1987, the song *Secret Love* put which legendary group back inside the Top 10?

MAY: *Get The Message* was a Top 10 hit for Bernard Sumner and Johnny Marr under what alias?

JUNE: Which member of The B-52's was a guest vocalist on R.E.M.'s Top 10 hit *Shiny Happy People*?

JULY: Who said there were *7 Ways To Love* on their one and only Official Singles Chart hit?

AUGUST: *Set Adrift On Memory Bliss* was a Top 3 hit for P.M. Dawn – which 1983 Spandau Ballet song was sampled throughout the track?

SEPTEMBER: Steve Wright and his Radio 1 afternoon-show posse had a Top 5 hit with a novelty song titled *I'll Be Back* – what alias did the team use for their performer credit on the record?

OCTOBER: Who sang about *Saltwater* and scored their first Official Singles Chart Top 10 hit since their debut in 1984?

NOVEMBER: The KLF briefly changed their name to The Justified Ancients Of Mu Mu and landed a Top 10 hit by reciting a list of towns and cities including Leeds, Hull, York and Bolton over the top of an electronic dance beat – what was the title of that bizarre track?

DECEMBER: Who was *Too Blind To See It*, according to the title of her Top 40 debut hit?

TOP 10: 2 NOVEMBER 1991

Fill in the blanks from this complete Official Singles
Chart Top 10. If the song title is listed, we're looking for
the band or artist that's missing. If the band or artist
is listed, we're looking for the missing song title.

1. (NEW) .... *THE FLY*

2. (6) VIC REEVES AND THE WONDER STUFF ....

3. (2) .... *GET READY FOR THIS*

4. (1) .... *(EVERYTHING I DO) I DO IT FOR YOU*

5. (4) KIRI TE KANAWA ....

6. (3) THE SCORPIONS ....

7. (5) MONTY PYTHON ....

8. (7) .... *INSANITY*

9. (NEW) .... *NO SON OF MINE*

10. (11) .... *GO*

Answers on page 261-2

All data below refers to positions achieved on the Official Singles Chart or (where relevant) the Official Albums Chart.

JANUARY: Icelandic band The Sugarcubes scored their only Top 20 song with the track *Hit* – who was their lead singer?

FEBRUARY: Name the dance act that made their Official Singles Chart debut straight inside the Top 10 with *It's A Fine Day*?

MARCH: Who suggested we should *Save The Best For Last* on their Top 3 hit?

APRIL: *Hold It Down* was the second of two Top 20 hits that year for which indie band?

MAY: Celine Dion and Peabo Bryson scored a Top 10 hit when they partnered up on the theme song to which animated Disney film?

JUNE: What was the title of the EP that gave Erasure their only Official Singles Chart Number 1?

JULY: Who were the two uncredited featured vocalists on *Shake Your Head*, a Top 10 hit for Was (Not Was)?

AUGUST: Which Cuban musician scored his biggest hit on the Official Singles Chart with the song *Just Another Day*?

SEPTEMBER: East 17 made their Top 40 debut with which song?

OCTOBER: *My Destiny* was the biggest hit single of the nineties for which superstar musician?

NOVEMBER: *Temptation* by Heaven 17 returned to the Top 10 thanks to a new remix by production team Brothers In Rhythm – in what year did the original version of the track first appear on the Official Singles Chart?

DECEMBER: Which group landed their fifth and final Top 10 hit with the song *Phorever People*?

TOP 10: 16 MAY 1992

Fill in the blanks from this complete Official Singles
Chart Top 10. If the song title is listed, we're looking for
the band or artist that's missing. If the band or artist
is listed, we're looking for the missing song title.

1. (1) .... PLEASE DON'T GO / GAME BOY

2. (2) SL2 ....

3. (7) .... HANG ON IN THERE BABY

4. (12) .... WORKAHOLIC

5. (3) RIGHT SAID FRED ....

6. (4) .... THE DAYS OF PEARLY SPENCER

7. (6) .... NOTHING ELSE MATTERS

8. (30) .... MY LOVIN'

9. (8) .... YOU'RE ALL THAT MATTERS TO ME

10. (NEW) .... COME PLAY WITH ME

Answers on page 262

All data below refers to positions achieved on the Official Singles Chart or (where relevant) the Official Albums Chart.

JANUARY: Which US rock band took The Commodores song *Easy* and renamed it *I'm Easy* for their successful Top 3 cover version?

FEBRUARY: *Sweet Harmony* was the one and only Top 10 hit for which group?

MARCH: After debuting in 1992 with *Everything About You*, name the Harry Chapin song that gave Ugly Kid Joe their second Top 10 hit on the Official Singles Chart.

APRIL: Name the *Coronation Steet* actor who landed a Top 20 hit with the song *One Voice*.

MAY: The double-A-sided release *Jump Around/Top 'O' The Morning To Ya* was the only Top 10 hit for which rap act?

JUNE: Name the band who took the song *Two Princes* into the Top 3.

JULY: Take That's seventh Top 40 single gave them their first Official Singles Chart Number 1 – what was the title?

AUGUST: Who claimed to have *The Key, The Secret* on their Number 2 hit?

SEPTEMBER: Pet Shop Boys scored their biggest single hit of the nineties with *Go West* at Number 2 for a fortnight, but which group first took the song to Number 15 in 1979?

OCTOBER: The Goodmen scored a Top 10 hit with *Give It Up* – which 1995 Number 1 song heavily sampled the track and made a subtle reference to 'good men' in the lyrics?

NOVEMBER: Name the band who took the song *Runaway Train* into the Top 10.

DECEMBER: The Number 1 Christmas chart-topper on the Official Singles Chart, for the first time in history, had the same title as the act performing it – what (and who) was it?

Answers on page 262

TOP 10: 24 APRIL 1993

Fill in the blanks from this complete Official Singles Chart Top 10. If the song title is listed, we're looking for the band or artist that's missing. If the band or artist is listed, we're looking for the missing song title.

1. (1) THE BLUEBELLS ....

2. (2) SNOW ....

3. (4) SUB SUB FEATURING MELANIE WILLIAMS ....

4. (11) .... *REGRET*

5. (5) .... *WHEN I'M GOOD AND READY*

6. (9) .... *U GOT 2 KNOW*

7. (8) JADE ....

8. (3) .... *OH CAROLINA*

9. (NEW) .... *I HAVE NOTHING*

10. (6) ROBIN S ....

Answers on page 262

All data below refers to positions achieved on the Official Singles Chart or (where relevant) the Official Albums Chart.

JANUARY: *Cornflake Girl* gave which musician her first Top 10 hit single?

FEBRUARY: Which legendary performer landed their biggest hit of the nineties with the Top 10 song *A Deeper Love*?

MARCH: Who said *The More You Ignore Me, The Closer I Get* on their fifteenth Top 40 solo hit?

APRIL: Prince changed his name to a symbol and scored his only Number 1 on the Official Singles Chart with which song?

MAY: A big-budget Levi jeans commercial helped the song *Inside* debut in the Top 5 in its first week of release, then climb to Number 1 a week later – name the band who performed the track.

JUNE: *Swamp Thing* by The Grid debuted inside the Top 20 – with which other group did The Grid's David Ball score a Number 1 single back in 1981?

JULY: A cover of Cameo's 1986 Top 3 hit *Word Up* gave which Scottish rock band their highest entry ever on the Official Singles Chart when it debuted at Number 8?

AUGUST: The Brand New Heavies featuring N'Dea Davenport covered *Midnight At The Oasis* and scored a Top 20 hit, but in what year did Maria Muldaur first take the song onto the chart?

SEPTEMBER: Which actor did the spoken-word verses on Blur's Top 10 hit *Parklife*?

OCTOBER: *Circle Of Life* was a Top 20 hit for Elton John – which animated Disney film featured the song on its soundtrack?

NOVEMBER: Pearl Jam scored their only Top 10 song on the Official Singles Chart – name the track.

DECEMBER: Which TV puppet duo arrived inside the Top 10 just in time for Christmas with *Them Girls Them Girls*?

TOP 10: 27 AUGUST 1994

Fill in the blanks from this complete Official Singles Chart Top 10. If the song title is listed, we're looking for the band or artist that's missing. If the band or artist is listed, we're looking for the missing song title.

1. (1) WET WET WET ....

2. (2) .... *CRAZY FOR YOU*

3. (5) RED DRAGON WITH BRIAN & TONY GOLD ....

4. (8) YOUSSOU N'DOUR FEATURING NENEH CHERRY ....

5. (4) .... *SEARCHING*

6. (3) .... *I SWEAR*

7. (6) DJ MIKO ....

8. (7) WARREN G & NATE DOGG ....

9. (11) .... *EIGHTEEN STRINGS*

10. (10) .... *LIVE FOREVER*

Answers on page 262

MONTH BY MONTH: 1995

All data below refers to positions achieved on the Official Singles Chart or (where relevant) the Official Albums Chart.

JANUARY: Name the Swedish group who spent three weeks at Number 1 with the song *Cotton Eye Joe*.

FEBRUARY: Irish composer and musician Bill Whelan scored a surprise Top 10 hit with the music from 1994's Eurovision Song Contest interval act – what was its name?

MARCH: *Independent Love Song* was the first and biggest of two Top 40 hits that year for which Hull-based duo?

APRIL: What was the one-word title of Tina Arena's Official Singles Chart debut hit?

MAY: An ad campaign for Guinness helped push *Guaglione* by Perez 'Prez' Prado to Number 2 and gave him his biggest hit in 40 years – can you name his 1955 Number 1 song?

JUNE: *Scream* was a Top 3 collaboration between which famous brother and sister?

JULY: Which 1967 Number 1 hit by The Monkees did Vic Reeves, Bob Mortimer and EMF take back into the Top 3 when they covered it?

AUGUST: The song *'74-'75* was the only Official Singles Chart hit for which American group?

SEPTEMBER: Berri's version of The *Sunshine After The Rain* was a Top 5 cover of a 1977 Top 10 hit for which singer?

OCTOBER: Kylie Minogue collaborated with which fellow Australian on the Top 20 duet *Where The Wild Roses Grow*?

NOVEMBER: Name the featured credited vocalist on the Number 1 song *Gangsta's Paradise* by rapper Coolio.

DECEMBER: The Mike Flowers Pops matched the original Official Singles Chart position of Number 2 with their novelty cover of which Oasis song?

TOP 10: 1 APRIL 1995

Fill in the blanks from this complete Official Singles Chart Top 10. If the song title is listed, we're looking for the band or artist that's missing. If the band or artist is listed, we're looking for the missing song title.

1. (2) .... *DON'T STOP (WIGGLE WIGGLE)*

2. (1) CHER, CHRISSIE HYNDE & NENEH CHERRY WITH ERIC CLAPTON ....

3. (6) .... *JULIA SAYS*

4. (3) .... *THINK TWICE*

5. (RE) .... *TWO CAN PLAY THAT GAME (K-KLASS REMIX)*

6. (RE) STRIKE ....

7. (NEW) .... *BABY IT'S YOU*

8. (5) .... *DON'T GIVE ME YOUR LIFE*

9. (4) FREAKPOWER ....

10. (11) .... *LET IT RAIN*

Answers on page 263

All data below refers to positions achieved on the Official Singles Chart or (where relevant) the Official Albums Chart.

JANUARY: The song *Sandstorm* was the first of seven Top 10 hits for which Merseyside band?

FEBRUARY: A big-budget ad campaign for Diet Coke sent which 1961 Etta James song into the Top 10 for the very first time?

MARCH: *Stupid Girl* reached the Top 5 on the Official Singles Chart for which group?

APRIL: There were two versions of the theme to the hit TV series *The X Files* sitting simultaneously in the Top 10 – one was by DJ Dado, but who did the other?

MAY: The Tony Rich Project made their Official Singles Chart debut and scored their only Top 10 hit with which song?

JUNE: Name the rapper who was credited on Peter Andre's debut Top 10 hit *Mysterious Girl*.

JULY: A 1996 remix of the dance anthem *Where Love Lives* gave which singer her biggest hit single?

AUGUST: *Peacock Suit* became the only solo Top 5 hit for which iconic British musician?

SEPTEMBER: What was the title of The Fugees' second Official Number 1 single of 1996 after *Killing Me Softly*?

OCTOBER: The band Deep Blue Something made their chart debut with which Number 1 song?

NOVEMBER: *Place Your Hands* was the biggest of nine Top 40 hit singles for which band?

DECEMBER: Who was the credited featured vocalist on Robert Miles' Top 3 hit *One And One*?

TOP 10: 4 MAY 1996

Fill in the blanks from this complete Official Singles Chart Top 10. If the song title is listed, we're looking for the band or artist that's missing. If the band or artist is listed, we're looking for the missing song title.

1. (NEW) .... _FASTLOVE_

2. (1) .... _RETURN OF THE MACK_

3. (3) .... _OOH AAH ... JUST A LITTLE BIT_

4. (2) .... _A DESIGN FOR LIFE_

5. (6) SUGGS FEATURING LOUCHIE LOU AND MICHIE ONE ....

6. (4) .... _THEY DON'T CARE ABOUT US_

7. (NEW) .... _BEFORE_

8. (NEW) .... _MOVE MOVE MOVE (THE RED TRIBE)_

9. (7) LISA MARIE EXPERIENCE ....

10. (NEW) .... _SALE OF THE CENTURY_

Answers on page 263

MONTH BY MONTH: 1997

All data below refers to positions achieved on the Official Singles Chart or (where relevant) the Official Albums Chart.

JANUARY: Derby-based musician Jyoti Mishra made his chart debut at Number 1 with the song *Your Woman* – what was his alias?

FEBRUARY: The track *Toxygene* debuted at Number 4 and became the biggest hit for which cult dance act?

MARCH: Name the 1991 dance anthem that scored its highest ever chart position when the Now Voyager Remix version reached Number 3.

APRIL: Aside from *Three Lions*, what's the only other song that put The Lightning Seeds into the Top 10 on the Official Singles Chart?

MAY: What three-word title gave the band Republica their only Top 10 hit?

JUNE: Savage Garden made their chart debut with which song, peaking on its first week of release at Number 11?

JULY: The dance anthem *Freed From Desire* debuted at Number 4 and became the biggest hit for which Italian singer-songwriter?

AUGUST: A re-issue of the debut hit for The Mamas & The Papas became a surprise Top 10 entry 31 years on – what was the song?

SEPTEMBER: Who said *Bentley's Gonna Sort You Out*, according to the title of their debut Top 40 hit?

OCTOBER: What was the other track listed as a double-A-sided release on Elton John's multi-million-selling reworking of *Candle In The Wind '97*?

NOVEMBER: The Top 10 song *Choose Life* by PF Project featured spoken-word contributions taken from the film *Trainspotting*, all of which were voiced by which Scottish actor?

DECEMBER: Which group appeared on the BBC's all-star charity version of *Perfect Day* at Number 1 while simultaneously having a Number 2 hit of their own with *Baby Can I Hold You*?

TOP 10: 7 JUNE 1997

Fill in the blanks from this complete Official Singles Chart Top 10. If the song title is listed, we're looking for the band or artist that's missing. If the band or artist is listed, we're looking for the missing song title.

1. (NEW) HANSON   ....

2. (1) ETERNAL FEATURING BEBE WINANS   ....

3. (NEW) ....   *PARANOID ANDROID*

4. (2) SARAH BRIGHTMAN AND ANDREA BOCELLI   ....

5. (4) ROSIE GAINES   ....

6. (3) OLIVE   ....

7. (5) THE REMBRANDTS   ....

8. (6) ....   *LOVEFOOL*

9. (RE) ....   *6 UNDERGROUND*

10. (NEW) TOBY BOURKE WITH GEORGE MICHAEL   ....

Answers on page 263

MONTH BY MONTH: 1998

All data below refers to positions achieved on the Official Singles Chart or (where relevant) the Official Albums Chart.

JANUARY: *Bamboogie* by Bamboo debuted at Number 2 – which 1975 KC & The Sunshine Band hit was sampled on the track?

FEBRUARY: The ten-year-old brother of Nick from the Backstreet Boys scored his second Top 10 hit in less than three months with the song *Crazy Little Party Girl* – name that kid.

MARCH: The cast of TV drama *Casualty* scored a Top 5 hit with a Children In Need charity cover version of *Everlasting Love* – name the group who spent a fortnight at Number 1 in 1968 with the same song.

APRIL: *Give A Little Love* was the only Top 10 hit single for an Irish crooner with a string of huge albums under her belt – who is he?

MAY: The Top 10 hit *Teardrop* by Massive Attack featured Elizabeth Fraser on vocals – with which acclaimed group did she make her Official Chart debut in April 1984?

JUNE: The song *Life* was the only Top 10 hit single for which BRIT Award-winning female singer?

JULY: Name Jamiroquai's only Official Singles Chart Number 1.

AUGUST: The Number 2 hit *Music Sounds Better With You* was a one-off project masterminded by Thomas Bangalter from Daft Punk along with fellow French musicians Alan Braxe and Benjamin 'Diamond' Cohen – what alias did the trio use on the record?

SEPTEMBER: What was Robbie Williams' first Official Singles Chart Number 1?

OCTOBER: Which Canadian scored their biggest ever hit with the Top 5 single *Thank U*?

NOVEMBER: Under what name did TV theme tune composer David Lowe reach the Top 3 with the song *Would You*?

DECEMBER: What was the title of the Spice Girls song which earned them their third consecutive Christmas Number 1 single?

Answers on page 264

TOP 10: 24 OCTOBER 1998

Fill in the blanks from this complete Official Singles Chart Top 10. If the song title is listed, we're looking for the band or artist that's missing. If the band or artist is listed, we're looking for the missing song title.

1. (NEW) SPACEDUST — ....

2. (NEW) .... — MORE THAN A WOMAN

3. (1) .... — GIRLFRIEND

4. (2) .... — ROLLERCOASTER

5. (4) AEROSMITH — ....

6. (NEW) .... — DAYSLEEPER

7. (3) .... — GANGSTER TRIPPIN'

8. (7) .... — PERFECT 10

9. (NEW) DRU HILL FEATURING REDMAN — ....

10. (NEW) .... — CAN'T KEEP THIS FEELING IN

Answers on page 264

All data below refers to positions achieved on the Official Singles Chart or (where relevant) the Official Albums Chart.

JANUARY: The All Seeing I teamed up with which legendary singer on the Top 10 hit *Walk Like A Panther*?

FEBRUARY: Which group suggested we should take the *National Express* on their only Top 10 hit single?

MARCH: What was the title of the song that gave American singer-songwriter Shawn Mullins a Top 10 hit?

APRIL: *You Get What You Give* became one of the year's biggest radio airplay favourites and the only Top 40 entry on the Official Singles Chart for which group?

MAY: Westlife made their Top 40 debut, going straight in at Number 1 with which song?

JUNE: Which Madonna hit debuted at Number 2 behind S Club 7 at Number 1 with *Bring It All Back*, and then featured in the film *Austin Powers: The Spy Who Sh*gged Me*?

JULY: What was the title of the Official Singles Chart debut for the band Semisonic?

AUGUST: Who were *Drinking In L.A.* on their Top 3 hit?

SEPTEMBER: A cover of the 1990 hit *There She Goes* by The La's was the second consecutive chart entry for which Texan group?

OCTOBER: Christina Aguilera made her Official Singles Chart debut with which Number 1 song?

NOVEMBER: What was the title of the first Number 1 single for boyband Five?

DECEMBER: *Steal My Sunshine* was a Top 10 hit for which group?

Answers on page 264

TOP 10: 18 SEPTEMBER 1999

Fill in the blanks from this complete Official Singles Chart Top 10. If the song title is listed, we're looking for the band or artist that's missing. If the band or artist is listed, we're looking for the missing song title.

1. (NEW) .... *WE'RE GOING TO IBIZA!*

2. (1) LOU BEGA ....

3. (2) DJ JEAN ....

4. (NEW) .... *MICKEY*

5. (NEW) THUNDERBUGS ....

6. (3) .... *(MUCHO MAMBO) SWAY*

7. (NEW) LEFTFIELD/BAMBAATAA ....

8. (4) .... *BAILAMOS*

9. (NEW) .... *MOVING*

10. (6) .... *I'VE GOT YOU*

Answers on page 264

SENSES WORKING OVERTIME

XTC said in their brilliant 1982 Top 10 hit that they could see, hear, smell, touch, and taste, and those five sensations can all be found on this next list of songs.

All you've got to do is name the bands and artists who brought these sensory moments direct to the Official Singles Chart.

1. *Smells Like Teen Spirit* [Number 7 in December 1991]

2. *I Can See For Miles* [Number 10 in November 1967]

3. *U Can't Touch This* [Number 3 in August 1990]

4. *Taste (Make It Shake)* [Number 2 in September 2019]

5. *Suddenly I See* [Number 12 in September 2005]

6. *Invisible Touch* [Number 15 in June 1986]

7. *When Will I See You Again?* [Number 1 in August 1974]

8. *The Taste Of Your Tears* [Number 11 in November 1985]

9. *I Heard It Through The Grapevine* [Number 1 in March 1969]

10. *The Bad Touch* [Number 4 in May 2000]

11. *See Emily Play* [Number 6 in July 1967]

12. *Touch* [Number 4 in December 2016]

13. *I Hear You Now* [Number 8 in February 1980]

14. *I Can See Clearly Now* [Number 5 in July 1972]

15. *Touch Me* (I Want Your Body) [Number 3 in April 1986]

16. *I Hear You Knocking* [Number 1 in November 1970]

17. *See It In A Boy's Eyes* [Number 5 in July 2004]

18. *I Touch Myself* [Number 10 in July 1991]

19. *I Can Hear The Grass Grow* [Number 5 in May 1967]

20. *See You* [Number 6 in March 1982]

INSTRUMENTAL HITS

Occasionally, an amazing instrumental hit arrives out of nowhere and pops up on the Official Singles Chart to surprise us all.

Orchestras, dance music producers, soundtrack composers, and even bagpipers – they're all here, along with many other musicians who didn't feel the need to add any vocals to their tunes.

See if you can identify the acts behind these memorable pieces of music.

1.   *Chariots Of Fire* [Number 12 in June 1981]

2.   *The Floral Dance* [Number 2 in December 1977]

3.   *Amazing Grace* [Number 1 in April 1972]

4.   *Crockett's Theme* [Number 2 in October 1987]

5.   *Chi Mai* (Theme From 'The Life And Times Of David Lloyd George') [Number 2 in April 1981]

6.   *Wonderful Land* [Number 1 in March 1962]

7.   *Pacific 707* [Number 10 in December 1989]

8.   *On The Rebound* [Number 1 in May 1961]

9.   *Portsmouth* [Number 3 in January 1977]

10. *Let There Be Drums* [Number 3 in January 1962]

11. *Axel F* [Number 2 in July 1985]

12. *Classical Gas* [Number 9 in October 1968]

13. *Theme from 'A Summer Place'* [Number 2 in March 1960]

14. *Chime* [Number 17 in March 1990]

15. *A Walk In The Black Forest* [Number 3 in August 1965]

16. *Clog Dance* [Number 17 in March 1979]

17. *Garden Party* [Number 17 in March 1983]

18. *Magic Fly* [Number 2 in September 1977]

19. *Lily Was Here* [Number 6 in March 1990]

20. *Oxygene Part IV* [Number 4 in September 1977]

Answers on page 264-5

HIT AFTER HIT:
MUSE

Place these five **MUSE** hits in their correct chronological order as they each appeared on the Official Singles Chart.

A. PLUG IN BABY

B. KNIGHTS OF CYDONIA

C. SUPERMASSIVE BLACK HOLE

D. UPRISING

E. STARLIGHT

Answers on page 265

ONE TO FIVE:
SHIRLEY BASSEY

Each of these **SHIRLEY BASSEY** hits achieved a different peak position on the Official Singles Chart – put them in the correct order, starting with Number 1 and working your way down to Number 5.

A. AS I LOVE YOU

B. WHAT NOW MY LOVE

C. AS LONG AS HE NEEDS ME

D. KISS ME HONEY HONEY KISS ME

E. SOMETHING

Answers on page 265

UNLUCKY FOR SOME

If you're superstitious, you might consider the number 13 to be unlucky. Well, it certainly was for this next set of performers, all of whom got stuck in that position on the Official Singles Chart with these great songs.

See how many of the bands and solo singers you can name.

1. *Love Will Tear Us Apart* [July 1980]

2. *I Love To Boogie* [July 1976]

3. *Love In An Elevator* [September 1989]

4. *I Am What I Am* [January 1984]

5. *Crying At The Discoteque* [December 2001]

6. *Sexy Boy* [February 1998]

7. *I'm Coming Out* [December 1980]

8. *Ready To Go* [March 1997]

9. *Promised You A Miracle* [May 1982]

10. *Glory Box* [January 1995]

11. *Lido Shuffle* [June 1977]

12. *Right Beside You* [September 1994]

13. *It's A Man's Man's Man's World* [July 1966]

14. *Hangin' On A String (Contemplating)* [March 1985]

15. *Always The Last To Know* [May 1992]

16. *Somebody's Else's Guy* [May 1984]

17. *Funky Cold Medina* [June 1989]

18. *Just Be Good To Me* [April 1984]

19. *Thunderstruck* [September 1990]

20. *Avalon* [June 1982]

Answers on page 265

WHERE THEM GIRLS AT?

David Guetta enlisted the help of Flo Rida and Nicki Minaj to ask that poignant question on their Top 3 hit back in 2011. That same year, Beyoncé claimed girls run the world, and it's certainly true that there was a period in pop when you couldn't move for girl groups all over the Official Singles Chart.

How many of them can you name from this list of 20 song titles?

1. *Whole Again* [Number 1 in February 2001]

2. *Bootie Call* [Number 1 in September 1998]

3. *No Good Advice* [Number 2 in May 2003]

4. *Waterfalls* [Number 4 in August 1995]

5. *I Quit* [Number 8 in May 1999]

6. *Finally Found* [Number 4 in September 1998]

7. *Scandalous* [Number 2 in March 2003]

8. *2 Become 1* [Number 1 in December 1996]

9. *Say My Name* [Number 3 in April 2000]

10. *Say It Again* [Number 6 in May 1999]

11. *Don't Walk Away* [Number 7 in April 1993]

12. *Angel Of Mine* [Number 4 in October 1997]

13. *We're Really Saying Something* [Number 17 in June 2000]

14. *Right Here* [Number 3 in September 1993]

15. *Perfect Bliss* [Number 18 in July 2001]

16. *Don't Let Go (Love)* [Number 5 in January 1997]

17. *Last One Standing* [Number 8 in July 2000]

18. *Life Ain't Easy* [Number 4 in May 1998]

19. *To You I Belong* [Number 1 in December 1998]

20. *Hole In The Head* [Number 1 in October 2003]

Answers on page 265

HIT AFTER HIT:
FIVE STAR

Place these eighties hits by **FIVE STAR** in their correct chronological order as they appeared on the Official Singles Chart during that decade.

A. FIND THE TIME

B. RAIN OR SHINE

C. THE SLIGHTEST TOUCH

D. SYSTEM ADDICT

E. CAN'T WAIT ANOTHER MINUTE

Answers on page 265

ONE TO FIVE:
ELLIE GOULDING

Each of these **ELLIE GOULDING** hits achieved a different peak position on the Official Singles Chart – put them in the correct order, starting with Number 1 and working your way down to Number 5.

A. ON MY MIND

B. HOW LONG WILL I LOVE YOU?

C. STARRY EYED

D. YOUR SONG

E. LOVE ME LIKE YOU DO

Answers on page 265

HIT AFTER HIT:
JASON DONOVAN

Place these five **JASON DONOVAN** hits in their correct chronological order as they each appeared on the Official Singles Chart.

A. TOO MANY BROKEN HEARTS

B. SEALED WITH A KISS

C. NOTHING CAN DIVIDE US

D. ANY DREAM WILL DO

E. EVERY DAY (I LOVE YOU MORE)

Answers on page 265

ONE TO FIVE:
P!NK

Each of these **P!NK** hits achieved a different peak position on the Official Singles Chart – put them in the correct order, starting with Number 1 and working your way down to Number 5.

A. WHO KNEW

B. STUPID GIRLS

C. WHAT ABOUT US

D. GET THE PARTY STARTED

E. JUST LIKE A PILL

Answers on page 265

NUMBER 11 HITS

If you thought the number 13 was unlucky, imagine how frustrating it must be if you're a musician who has a song stuck just outside the Top 10 on the Official Singles Chart.

Here are 20 poor souls who couldn't quite crack through, even though every one of these excellent tunes certainly deserved to.

Can you name the bands and artists?

1. *Superstition* [February 1973]

2. *Coffee + TV* [July 1999]

3. *Greased Lightnin'* [December 1978]

4. *Island Of Lost Souls* [June 1982]

5. *Big Yellow Taxi* [August 1970]

6. *E=MC2* [April 1986]

7. *The Zephyr Song* [November 2002]

8. *Something Got Me Started* [September 1991]

9. *Drop The Pilot* [March 1983]

10. *Lonely Boy* [May 1977]

11. *Big Log* [August 1983]

12. *Shakermaker* [July 1994]

13. *Stacy's Mom* [March 2004]

14. *Headlines (Friendship Never Ends)* [December 2007]

15. *Suicide Blonde* [September 1990]

16. *Dream A Little Dream Of Me* [September 1968]

17. *Young Turks* [December 1981]

18. *Hazy Shade Of Winter* [March 1988]

19. *Ironic* [April 1996]

20. *Let It Go* [May 2014]

Answers on page 265-6

SUPERSTAR SPOTLIGHT:
QUEEN & FREDDIE MERCURY

1. Queen made their Official Singles Chart debut in 1974 with which song?

2. The band released just one single in 1985 and it became an instant Top 10 hit in November that year – name it.

3. When Queen's *Bohemian Rhapsody* was re-issued shortly after Freddie Mercury's death in 1991, which other song was part of its double-A-sided release?

4. How many Number 1 hits did Queen achieve on the Official Singles Chart during Freddie Mercury's lifetime, and can you name the final one, which spent just a week at the top in January 1991?

5. What was the title of Freddie Mercury's first solo Top 10 hit, released in September 1984?

6. Place these five Queen hits in their correct chronological order as they each appeared on the Official Singles Chart during the 1970s and 1980s.

   a. *I Want To Break Free*
   b. *Another One Bites The Dust*
   c. *A Kind Of Magic*
   d. *You're My Best Friend*
   e. *Crazy Little Thing Called Love*

Answers on page 266

HIT AFTER HIT:
IRON MAIDEN

Place these eighties hits by **IRON MAIDEN** in their correct chronological order as they appeared on the Official Singles Chart during that decade.

A. RUN TO THE HILLS

B. CAN I PLAY WITH MADNESS

C. THE EVIL THAT MEN DO

D. FLIGHT OF ICARUS

E. THE NUMBER OF THE BEAST

Answers on page 266

ONE TO FIVE:
STATUS QUO

Each of these **STATUS QUO** hits achieved a different peak position on the Official Singles Chart – put them in the correct order, starting with Number 1 and working your way down to Number 5.

A. IN THE ARMY NOW

B. ROCKIN' ALL OVER THE WORLD

C. DOWN DOWN

D. CAROLINE

E. WHATEVER YOU WANT

Answers on page 266

FOR THOSE ABOUT TO ROCK (WE SALUTE YOU)

Every one of these 40 titles is a solid rock anthem that appeared on the Official Singles Chart and was recorded by one of the biggest, best, or most-influential guitar bands of all time.

Name the legends who were responsible for each of these tracks.

1. *Livin' On A Prayer* [Number 4 in December 1986]

2. *Rockin' All Over The World* [Number 3 in November 1977]

3. *Purple Haze* [Number 3 in May 1967]

4. *Whole Lotta Love* [Number 21 in September 1997]

5. *Sweet Child O' Mine* [Number 6 in June 1989]

6. *Ace Of Spades* [Number 15 in November 1980]

7. *Bring Your Daughter ... To The Slaughter* [Number 1 in January 1991]

8. *Won't Get Fooled Again* [Number 9 in August 1971]

9. *Living After Midnight* [Number 12 in April 1980]

10. *Enter Sandman* [Number 5 in August 1991]

11. *Duality* [Number 15 in June 2004]

12. *I Surrender* [Number 3 in February 1981]

13. *Wishing Well* [Number 7 in February 1973]

14. *American Idiot* [Number 3 in September 2004]

15. *Smoke On The Water* [Number 21 in May 1977]

16. *Sunshine Of Your Love* [Number 25 in October 1968]

17. *Don't Stop Me Now* [Number 9 in March 1979]

18. *Jump* [Number 7 in March 1984]

19. *Anarchy In The U.K.* [Number 38 in December 1976]

20. *Best Of You* [Number 4 in June 2005]

21. *It's Only Rock 'N Roll (But I Like It)* [Number 10 in August 1974]

22. *Paranoid* [Number 4 in October 1970]

23. *Crazy Crazy Nights* [Number 4 in October 1987]

24. *Rock 'N' Roll Ain't Noise Pollution* [Number 15 in December 1980]

25. *Gimme All Your Lovin'* [Number 10 in November 1984]

26. *White Riot* [Number 38 in April 1977]

27. *Come As You Are* [Number 9 in March 1992]

28. *Abacab* [Number 9 in September 1981]

29. *Ignorance* [Number 14 in September 2009]

30. *Give It Away* [Number 9 in February 1994]

31. *Waiting For An Alibi* [Number 9 in March 1979]

32. *Where The Streets Have No Name* [Number 4 in September 1987]

33. *In The End* [Number 8 in October 2001]

34. *Alive* [Number 16 in February 1992]

35. *Girls, Girls, Girls* [Number 26 in August 1987]

36. *Midlife Crisis* [Number 10 in June 1992]

37. *Fool For Your Loving* [Number 13 in May 1980]

38. *Been Caught Stealing* [Number 34 in March 1991]

39. *Let's Get Rocked* [Number 2 in April 1992]

40. *Dude (Looks Like A Lady)* [Number 20 in March 1990]

Answers on page 266

HIT AFTER HIT:
BON JOVI

Place these five **BON JOVI** hits in their correct chronological order as they each appeared on the Official Singles Chart.

A. IT'S MY LIFE

B. WANTED DEAD OR ALIVE

C. WHO SAYS YOU CAN'T GO HOME?

D. IN THESE ARMS

E. KEEP THE FAITH

Answers on page 266

ONE TO FIVE:
BRYAN ADAMS

Each of these **BRYAN ADAMS** hits achieved a different peak position on the Official Singles Chart – put them in the correct order, starting with Number 1 and working your way down to Number 5.

A. HERE I AM

B. WHEN YOU'RE GONE (FEATURING MELANIE C)

C. DON'T GIVE UP (AS FEATURED ARTIST WITH CHICANE)

D. PLEASE FORGIVE ME

E. HAVE YOU EVER REALLY LOVED A WOMAN?

Answers on page 266

MADE IN WALES

Throughout the first 70 years of the Official Singles Chart, many great Welsh bands and iconic solo performers have delivered countless hits, so we've gathered 20 of the best (including a few you'd probably forgotten all about) to test you further.

How many names can you correctly identify from these song titles?

1.   *It's Not Unusual* [Number 1 in March 1965]

2.   *This Ole House* [Number 1 in March 1981]

3.   *Have A Nice Day* [Number 5 in June 2001]

4.   *Walking In The Air* [Number 5 in December 1985]

5.   *Goldfinger* [Number 21 in October 1964]

6.   *Everything Must Go* [Number 5 in August 1996]

7.   *This Is My Song* [Number 2 in March 1967]

8.   *Golden Retriever* [Number 13 in July 2003]

9.   *Dead From The Waist Down* [Number 7 in April 1999]

10.   *Those Were The Days* [Number 1 in September 1968]

11.   *They* [Number 6 in March 2005]

12.   *I Love You Always Forever* [Number 5 in October 1996]

13.   *Rain On Your Parade* [Number 15 in November 2008]

14.   *Born To Be With You* [Number 5 in July 1973]

15.   *Guns Don't Kill People, Rappers Do* [Number 3 in August 2004]

16.   *68 Guns* [Number 17 in October 1983]

17.   *Tell Laura I Love Her* [Number 1 in September 1960]

18.   *Call My Name* [Number 10 in October 2005]

19.   *Come And Get It* [Number 4 in January 1970]

20.   *Holding Out For A Hero* [Number 2 in September 1985]

Answers on page 266-7

SUPERSTAR SPOTLIGHT:

1. Oasis made their Official Singles Chart debut in 1994 with which song?

2. With which London-based electronic dance act did Liam Gallagher score a Top 20 hit in December 2002 titled *Scorpio Rising*?

3. Name the Oasis song that got stuck at Number 2 in August 1995 during the famous Britpop battle that saw *Country House* by Blur top the Official Singles Chart ahead of Noel and Liam.

4. What was the title of the band's last ever Top 10 hit before they split in 2009?

5. The debut hit from Noel Gallagher's High Flying Birds made a brief appearance inside the Top 20 in September 2011 – what was the title of the track?

6. Place these five Oasis hits in their correct chronological order as they each appeared on the Official Singles Chart during the nineties and noughties.

    a. *Go Let It Out*
    b. *The Importance Of Being Idle*
    c. *The Hindu Times*
    d. *Some Might Say*
    e. *Stand By Me*

Answers on page 267

HIT AFTER HIT:
SPICE GIRLS

Place these nineties hits by the **SPICE GIRLS** in their correct chronological order as they appeared on the Official Singles Chart during that decade.

A. SAY YOU'LL BE THERE

B. VIVA FOREVER

C. TOO MUCH

D. SPICE UP YOUR LIFE

E. 2 BECOME 1

Answers on page 267

ONE TO FIVE:
BACKSTREET BOYS

Each of these **BACKSTREET BOYS** hits achieved a different peak position on the Official Singles Chart – put them in the correct order, starting with Number 1 and working your way down to Number 5.

A. SHAPE OF MY HEART

B. LARGER THAN LIFE

C. I WANT IT THAT WAY

D. ALL I HAVE TO GIVE

E. AS LONG AS YOU LOVE ME

Answers on page 267

I'LL BE MISSING YOU

Just as we did earlier in the book with a bunch of eighties songs, we've done it again here for a selection of great hits from the nineties – all the words that were originally listed in brackets when each of these titles appeared on the Official Singles Chart have been removed.

We've listed the band or artist along with their peak position and year, so all you've got to do, once again, is fill in the blanks.

1. *I'd Do Anything For Love (___ ___ ___ ___ ___)*
    Meat Loaf [Number 1 in October 1993]

2. *Pretty Fly (___ ___ ___ ___)*
    The Offspring [Number 1 in January 1999]

3. *(___ ___) The Same Thing*
    Belinda Carlisle [Number 6 in November 1990]

4. *Slam Dunk (___ ___)*
    Five [Number 10 in December 1997]

5. *Hear The Drummer (___ ___)*
    Chad Jackson [Number 3 in June 1990]

6. *Don't Stop (___ ___)*
    The Outhere Brothers [Number 1 in April 1995]

7. *Senza Una Donna (___ ___ ___)*
    Zucchero featuring Paul Young [Number 4 in May 1991]

8. *(___ ___ ___ ___) Devotion*
    Nomad featuring MC Mikee Freedom [Number 2 in February 1991]

9. *Sweat (___ ___ ___ ___ ___ ___)*
    Inner Circle [Number 3 in May 1993]

10. *Get Up! (___ ___ ___ ___ ___)*
    Technotronic featuring Ya Kid K [Number 3 in February 1990]

11. *Time To Say Goodbye (___ ___ ___)*
    Sarah Brightman and Andrea Bocelli [Number 2 in May 1997]

12. *Tom Traubert's Blues (___ ___)*
    Rod Stewart [Number 6 in December 1992]

13. *No Good (___ ___ ___)*
    The Prodigy [Number 4 in June 1994]

14. *Street Spirit (___ ___)*
    Radiohead [Number 5 in February 1996]

15. *(___ ___) Sway*
    Shaft [Number 2 in September 1999]

16. *Because I Love You (___ ___ ___)*
    Stevie B [Number 6 in March 1991]

17. *Ain't No Love (___ ___ ___)*
    Sub Sub featuring Melanie Williams [Number 3 in April 1993]

18. *Good Riddance (___ ___ ___ ___)*
    Green Day [Number 11 in January 1998]

19. *Touch Me (___ ___ ___)*
    Cathy Dennis [Number 5 in May 1991]

20. *It Keeps Rainin' (___ ___ ___ ___)*
    Bitty McLean [Number 2 in September 1993]

21. *(___ ___ ___) Piece Of My Heart*
    Erma Franklin [Number 9 in October 1992]

22. *The Bomb! (___ ___ ___ ___ ___ ___)*
    Kenny 'Dope' Presents The Bucketheads [Number 5 in March 1995]

23. *Whoomph! (___ ___ ___)*
    Clock [Number 4 in July 1995]

24. *Scatman (___ ___ ___ ___ ___ ___)*
    Scatman John [Number 3 in May 1995]

25. *Everybody's Free (___ ___ ___)*
Baz Luhrmann [Number 1 in June 1999]

26. *You Don't Love Me (___ ___ ___)*
Dawn Penn [Number 3 in June 1994]

27. *Protect Your Mind (___ ___ ___ ___ ___ ___)*
DJ Sakin & Friends [Number 4 in February 1999]

28. *(___ ___ ___) Maria*
Ricky Martin [Number 6 in September 1997]

29. *Stay (___ ___ ___)*
Lisa Loeb [Number 6 in October 1994]

30. *Doo Wop (___ ___)*
Lauryn Hill [Number 3 in October 1998]

31. *Hello (___ ___ ___ ___)*
Shakespears Sister [Number 14 in November 1992]

32. *9pm (___ ___ ___)*
ATB [Number 1 in July 1999]

33. *Professional Widow (___ ___ ___ ___ ___)*
Tori Amos [Number 1 in January 1997]

34. *Someday (___ ___ ___)*
Lisa Stansfield [Number 10 in January 1993]

35. *Hard Knock Life (___ ___)*
Jay-Z [Number 2 in December 1998]

36. *We Like To Party! (___ ___)*
The Vengaboys [Number 3 in March 1999]

37. *Se A Vida E (___ ___ ___ ___ ___)*
Pet Shop Boys [Number 8 in August 1996]

38. *Ghetto Supastar (___ ___ ___ ___ ___)*
Pras Michel featuring ODB & Mya [Number 2 in July 1998]

39. *Everybody (___ ___)*
Backstreet Boys [Number 3 in August 1997]

40. *Re-Rewind (___ ___ ___ ___ ___)*
Artful Dodger featuring Craig David [Number 2 in December 1999]

Answers on page 267

HIT AFTER HIT:
TAKE THAT

Place these nineties hits by **TAKE THAT** in their correct chronological order as they appeared on the Official Singles Chart during that decade.

A. BABE

B. PRAY

C. SURE

D. NEVER FORGET

E. BACK FOR GOOD

Answers on page 267

ONE TO FIVE:
WESTLIFE

Each of these **WESTLIFE** hits achieved a different peak position on the Official Singles Chart – put them in the correct order, starting with Number 1 and working your way down to Number 5.

A. WORLD OF OUR OWN

B. HEY WHATEVER

C. BOP BOP BABY

D. HOME

E. WHAT MAKES A MAN

Answers on page 267

AROUND THE WORLD

Let's take a musical trip across the planet, stopping off at 20 countries that have all been immortalized in the titles of Official Singles Chart hits from the 1950s to the 2020s.

Try to identify the performers who brought us these songs.

1. *Princess Of China* [Number 4 in June 2012]

2. *Uncle John From Jamaica* [Number 6 in July 2000]

3. *A New England* [Number 7 in February 1985]

4. *Cambodia* [Number 12 in December 1981]

5. *Don't Cry For Me Argentina* [Number 1 in February 1977]

6. *This Is America* [Number 6 in May 2018]

7. *Cuba* [Number 12 in March 1980]

8. *Peru* [Number 2 in February 2022]

9. *Big In Japan* [Number 8 in September 1984]

10. *Cry India* [Number 19 in September 1995]

11. *Greece* [Number 8 in July 2020]

12. *Lost In France* [Number 9 in November 1976]

13. *Mum's Gone To Iceland* [Number 34 in February 1997]

14. *Papua New Guinea* [Number 22 in May 1992]

15. *The Lebanon* [Number 11 in May 1984]

16. *When Mexico Gave Up The Rhumba* [Number 6 in November 1956]

17. *Ecuador* [Number 2 in July 1997]

18. *On A Little Street In Singapore* [Number 20 in June 1978]

19. *Barbados* [Number 1 in August 1975]

20. *Australia* [Number 7 in December 1996]

Answers on page 267

DON'T LET IT SHOW ON YOUR FACE

It's surprising to see how many times this part of the body has appeared in song titles during the first 70 years of the Official Singles Chart. The question is, how many of the 20 bands and artists on this list you can identify?

To help you along, the peak position and year of each is in brackets.

1. *Poker Face* [Number 1 in March 2009]

2. *Can't Feel My Face* [Number 3 in August 2015]

3. *The First Time Ever I Saw Your Face* [Number 14 in July 1972]

4. *Eyes Without A Face* [Number 18 in August 1984]

5. *The Face* [Number 13 in February 1990]

6. *Baby Face* [Number 2 in January 1959]

7. *Faces* [Number 8 in September 1993]

8. *My Brave Face* [Number 18 in May 1989]

9. *Take That Look Off Your Face* [Number 3 in March 1980]

10. *Wash Your Face In My Sink* [Number 16 in August 1990]

11. *Born With A Smile On My Face* [Number 2 in August 1974]

12. *If I Never See Your Face Again* [Number 28 in June 2008]

13. *In Yer Face* [Number 9 in February 1991]

14. *Angels With Dirty Faces* [Number 19 in June 1978]

15. *Face To Face* [Number 21 in July 1992]

16. *2 Faced* [Number 3 in July 2000]

17. *Smiley Faces* [Number 10 in July 2006]

18. *Angel Face* [Number 4 in April 1974]

19. *Nice Legs, Shame About The Face* [Number 19 in May 1979]

20. *Shaddap You Face* [Number 1 in February 1981]

Answers on page 268

SOMETHING IN COMMON

Bobby Brown and Whitney Houston had a Top 20 hit with a song bearing that title in January 1994, and it got us thinking about the various musicians and performers who've appeared on the Official Singles Chart over the years, many of whom often share the same familiar surname.

Can you figure out the link for each of these 20 sets of stars?

1. Joe – Freddie – Janet

2. Edwyn – Judy – Phil

3. Jilted – Scatman – Elton

4. Aled – Howard – Grace

5. Barry – Snowy – Tony Joe

6. Laurie – Lynn – Angry

7. Tina – Gary – Dorothy

8. Joe – James – Ian

9. Will – Hurricane – Jorja

10. Amii – Jermaine – Andy

11. Linda – CJ – Leona

12. Deniece – Andy – Vanessa

13. Eddy – Amy – David

14. Neil – Paul – Will

15. Cat – Rachel – Ray

16. Kenny – Nicky – Evelyn

17. Holly – Andreas – Marv

18. Tom – Scott – Alan

19. Dean – Ricky – Billy Ray

20. Roger – Steve – Frankie

Answers on page 268

TAKE ME TO THE HOSPITAL

Ailments, illness and songs about being rather poorly – here are 20 tunes that need some sort of urgent medical attention. So, get down to the pop clinic and diagnose the correct band or artist, then match each of them to this list of titles.

1.   *Just Like A Pill* [Number 1 in September 2002]

2.   *Healing Hands* [Number 1 in June 1990]

3.   *So Sick* [Number 1 in April 2006]

4.   *Fever* [Number 5 in September 1958]

5.   *Doctor! Doctor!* [Number 3 in February 1984]

6.   *The Bitterest Pill (I Ever Had To Swallow)* [Number 2 in September 1982]

7.   *Bad Medicine* [Number 17 in October 1988]

8.   *Cardiac Arrest* [Number 14 in March 1982]

9.   *Bloodstream* [Number 2 in April 2015]

10. *I Need A Doctor* [Number 8 in April 2011]

11. *Purple Pills* [Number 2 in July 2001]

12. *Looking Through Patient Eyes* [Number 11 in March 1993]

13. *New Kind Of Medicine* [Number 14 in July 1998]

14. *Doctor's Orders* [Number 7 in May 1974]

15. *Shake The Disease* [Number 18 in June 1985]

16. *Doctor Pressure* [Number 3 in September 2005]

17. *Smokers Outside The Hospital Doors* [Number 7 in June 2007]

18. *Girlfriend In A Coma* [Number 13 in August 1987]

19. *Night Nurse* [Number 13 in September 1997]

20. *Doctor Jones* [Number 1 in February 1998]

Answers on page 268

SUPERSTAR SPOTLIGHT:
MICHAEL JACKSON

1. In what year did The Jackson Five make their Official Singles Chart debut with the Number 2 hit *I Want You Back*?

2. Name the only Number 1 song on the Official Singles Chart for the Jacksons.

3. How many Top 10 hits did Michael pull from his 1979 album *Off The Wall*?

4. When the song *Thriller* was eventually released as a single in November 1983, what was its peak chart position?

5. Michael had the Christmas Number 1 on the Official Singles Chart in 1995 – name that hit.

6. Each of these solo hits by Michael achieved a different peak position on the Official Singles Chart – put them in the correct order, starting with Number 1 and working your way down to Number 5.

    a. *Heal The World*
    b. *Rockin' Robin*
    c. *Got To Be There*
    d. *Dirty Diana*
    e. *One Day In Your Life*

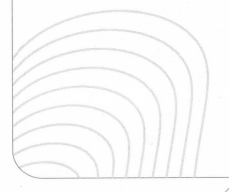

Answers on page 268

FOOD FOR THOUGHT

Feeling peckish? You certainly will be by the time you try to name the 20 acts who brought these moments of foody heaven to the Official Singles Chart – good luck naming them all!

1. *Watermelon Sugar* [Number 4 in August 2020]

2. *Popcorn* [Number 5 in August 1972]

3. *Milkshake* [Number 2 in January 2004]

4. *Brown Sugar* [Number 2 in May 1971]

5. *Green Onions* [Number 7 in January 1980]

6. *Banana Splits* [Number 7 in May 1979]

7. *Cream* [Number 15 in September 1991]

8. *Toast* [Number 18 in November 1978]

9. *Honey* [Number 3 in September 1997]

10. *Sugar And Spice* [Number 2 in November 1963]

11. *Peaches* [Number 8 in April 1996]

12. *Chocolate* [Number 6 in July 2004]

13. *Butter* [Number 3 in June 2021]

14. *Jambalaya* [Number 12 in March 1974]

15. *Icing On The Cake* [Number 14 in June 1985]

16. *Passionfruit* [Number 3 in April 2017]

17. *Lollipop* [Number 2 in May 1958]

18. *Bread And Butter* [Number 15 in October 1964]

19. *Peanut Butter Jelly* [Number 8 in September 2015]

20. *The Chicken Song* [Number 1 in May 1986]

HIT AFTER HIT:
JAMIROQUAI

Place these nineties hits by **JAMIROQUAI** in their correct chronological order as they appeared on the Official Singles Chart during that decade.

A. VIRTUAL INSANITY

B. ALRIGHT

C. COSMIC GIRL

D. SPACE COWBOY

E. CANNED HEAT

Answers on page 269

ONE TO FIVE:
RIHANNA

Each of these **RIHANNA** hits achieved a different peak position on the Official Singles Chart – put them in the correct order, starting with Number 1 and working your way down to Number 5.

A. DON'T STOP THE MUSIC

B. DISTURBIA

C. SHUT UP AND DRIVE

D. PON DE REPLAY

E. DIAMONDS

Answers on page 269

ANYONE WHO HAD A HEART

The heart is one body part that seems to be referenced in music more than any other. In fact, more than 20 different Number 1 songs mentioned it in the first 70 years of the Official Singles Chart, including Cilla Black's in February 1964.

A few of those big titles are included here, mixed in with several other great songs.

How many of the performers can you correctly identify?

1. *Total Eclipse Of The Heart* [Number 1 in March 1983]

2. *Groove Is In The Heart* [Number 2 in September 1990]

3. *Heart Of Glass* [Number 1 in February 1979]

4. *Each Time You Break My Heart* [Number 5 in December 1986]

5. *My Heart Will Go On* [Number 1 in February 1998]

6. *Heart Of Gold* [Number 10 in April 1972]

7. *Nothing Breaks Like A Heart* [Number 2 in January 2019]

8. *Achy Breaky Heart* [Number 3 in August 1992]

9. *Burning Heart* [Number 5 in March 1986]

10. *Heart On My Sleeve* [Number 6 in June 1976]

11. *Somewhere In My Heart* [Number 3 in June 1988]

12. *Another Nail In My Heart* [Number 17 in March 1980]

13. *Un-Break My Heart* [Number 2 in December 1996]

14. *All Of My Heart* [Number 5 in September 1982]

15. *My Simple Heart* [Number 9 in December 1979]

16. *Tell It To My Heart* [Number 3 in February 1988]

17. *Bonfire Heart* [Number 4 in October 2013]

18. *Break My Heart* [Number 6 in April 2020]

19. *Give Me Back My Heart* [Number 4 in April 1982]

20. *A Good Heart* [Number 1 in November 1985]

Answers on page 269

HIT AFTER HIT:
BOYZONE

Place these nineties hits by **BOYZONE** in their correct chronological order as they appeared on the Official Singles Chart during that decade.

A. FATHER AND SON

B. WORDS

C. LOVE ME FOR A REASON

D. ALL THAT I NEED

E. PICTURE OF YOU

Answers on page 269

ONE TO FIVE:
RONAN KEATING

Each of these **RONAN KEATING** hits achieved a different peak position on the Official Singles Chart – put them in the correct order, starting with Number 1 and working your way down to Number 5.

A. WHEN YOU SAY NOTHING AT ALL

B. THE LONG GOODBYE

C. WE'VE GOT TONIGHT (FEATURING LULU)

D. LOVIN' EACH DAY

E. I LOVE IT WHEN WE DO

Answers on page 269

THE OFFICIAL CHARTS' MUSIC QUIZ BOOK

SPOTLIGHT:
2000s

MONTH BY MONTH: 2000

All data below refers to positions achieved on the Official Singles Chart or (where relevant) the Official Albums Chart.

JANUARY: What was the title of the Manic Street Preachers song that became the first new Number 1 song of the 2000s?

FEBRUARY: Which band scored their only Top 3 hit single with *The Great Beyond*?

MARCH: The song *Money* was a Top 5 collaboration between Jamelia and which Jamaican reggae star?

APRIL: Which member of TLC was the featured guest rapper on *Never Be The Same Again*, a Number 1 for Melanic C?

MAY: Mandy Moore made her debut on the Official Singles Chart with a Top 10 hit – what was the one-word title of that song?

JUNE: Who duetted with Whitney Houston on the Top 10 hit *If I Told You That*?

JULY: The Corrs scored their only Number 1 on the Official Singles Chart – what was its one-word title?

AUGUST: Bomfunk MC's made their chart debut at Number 2 with *Freestyler* while their friend and fellow countryman Darude was inside the Top 20 with his song *Sandstorm* – what nationality are both acts?

SEPTEMBER: Which girl group made their debut with the Top 10 hit *Overload*?

OCTOBER: What was the canine-themed title of the Baha Men's biggest hit on the Official Singles Chart?

NOVEMBER: Which BBC kids TV characters got to Number 5 with their song that was titled *Number 1*?

DECEMBER: Bob The Builder had the Christmas Number 1 on the Official Singles Chart – name his song.

TOP 10: 25 MARCH 2000

Fill in the blanks from this complete Official Singles Chart Top 10. If the song title is listed, we're looking for the band or artist that's missing. If the band or artist is listed, we're looking for the missing song title.

1. (NEW) .... BAG IT UP

2. (NEW) .... ALL THE SMALL THINGS

3. (1) CHICANE FEATURING BRYAN ADAMS ....

4. (NEW) .... KILLER

5. (2) .... AMERICAN PIE

6. (NEW) DR DRE FEATURING SNOOP DOGGY DOGG ....

7. (3) .... PURE SHORES

8. (5) LENE MARLIN ....

9. (4) TOM JONES AND STEREOPHONICS ....

10. (6) .... SHALALA LALA

Answers on page 269

MONTH BY MONTH: 2001

All data below refers to positions achieved on the Official Singles Chart or (where relevant) the Official Albums Chart.

JANUARY: What was the title of Limp Bizkit's only Number 1 single?

FEBRUARY: After featuring on Eminem's Number 1 song *Stan* in December 2000, who made their first ever appearance on the chart as an artist in her own right with the Top 5 hit, *Here With Me*?

MARCH: Ricky Martin teamed up with Christina Aguilera for a Top 5 hit song – what was the title?

APRIL: Which rap legend suggested you should *Get Ur Freak On*, according to the title of their Top 5 hit?

MAY: Geri Halliwell's cover of the song *It's Raining Men* spent a fortnight at Number 1, but in what year did the original version by The Weather Girls peak at Number 2?

JUNE: The Ringbang Remix of which 1983 Eddy Grant hit put the song back inside the Top 5?

JULY: *Castles In The Sky* was the first of three consecutive Top 10 hits for which Belgian trance group?

AUGUST: Who was the only woman that got *21 Seconds* on the mic on So Solid Crew's Official Singles Chart Number 1?

SEPTEMBER: Louise took her cover of *Stuck In The Middle With You* into the Top 5, but which group first placed the song in the Top 10 in June 1973?

OCTOBER: *Thinking It Over* was the debut hit for a group formed by wannabes from ITV's original *Popstars* series – who were they?

NOVEMBER: The boyband Five bowed out with their farewell Top 10 hit single – what was its title?

DECEMBER: Name the Oscar-winning actress who performed the song *What If* and scored a surprise Top 10 hit.

TOP 10: 14 JULY 2001

Fill in the blanks from this complete Official Singles
Chart Top 10. If the song title is listed, we're looking for
the band or artist that's missing. If the band or artist
is listed, we're looking for the missing song title.

1. (NEW) ROGER SANCHEZ ....

2. (2) CHRISTINA AGUILERA /
LIL' KIM / MYA / P!NK ....

3. (NEW) .... *A LITTLE RESPECT*

4. (NEW) OPM ....

5. (1) .... *THE WAY TO YOUR LOVE*

6. (3) .... *U REMIND ME*

7. (4) SHAGGY FEATURING RAYVON ....

8. (5) .... *THERE YOU'LL BE*

9. (6) *19-2000*

10. (7) .... *ALL I WANT*

Answers on page 270

All data below refers to positions achieved on the Official Singles Chart or (where relevant) the Official Albums Chart.

JANUARY: After previously topping the chart in December 2001, Daniel Bedingfield returned to Number 1 this month with his debut single – name it.

FEBRUARY: What was Afroman's Top 10 follow-up to his 2001 Number 1 debut *Because I Got High*?

MARCH: Will Young won ITV's *Pop Idol* and he quickly released a double-A-sided single that became the biggest seller of the noughties – one song was *Evergreen*, but what was the other featured track?

APRIL: *Me Julie* was a Top 3 collaboration that brought together comedian Sacha Baron Cohen's character Ali G with which reggae star?

MAY: The Canadian rock band Nickelback made their chart debut with which Top 5 song?

JUNE: *The Logical Song* by German techno group Scooter was based on the old Supertramp hit of the same name, but in what year did the original reach the Top 10?

JULY: After performing *Your Song* on Baz Luhrmann's *Moulin Rouge* soundtrack, which Italian opera star teamed up with Elton John for a new cover version of that song and reached the Top 5?

AUGUST: *Pop Idol* finalist Darius confounded the critics and debuted at Number 1 on the Official Singles Chart with which song?

SEPTEMBER: Madonna's 1986 Number 1 *Papa Don't Preach* returned to the chart thanks to a new cover version by which female star?

OCTOBER: After making his chart debut in 1977 with guitarist Wild Willy Barrett on the track *Really Free*, which song gave John Otway his one and only Top 10 hit?

NOVEMBER: Who took the Bryan Adams minor 1985 hit *Heaven* all the way to Number 1 in the form of a new cover version designed for the dancefloor?

DECEMBER: What was the title of the Christmas Number 1 album by Robbie Williams that featured the Official Singles Chart Top 10 hit *Feel*?

Answers on page 270

TOP 10: 9 FEBRUARY 2002

Fill in the blanks from this complete Official Singles
Chart Top 10. If the song title is listed, we're looking for
the band or artist that's missing. If the band or artist
is listed, we're looking for the missing song title.

1. (1) ENRIQUE IGLESIAS ....

2. (3) .... GET THE PARTY STARTED

3. (2) .... CAUGHT IN THE MIDDLE

4. (5) .... OVERPROTECTED

5. (8) PURETONE ....

6. (6) .... ALWAYS ON TIME

7. (7) FLIP & FILL FEATURING KELLY LLORENNA ....

8. (4) .... MY SWEET LORD

9. (9) .... AM TO PM

10. (11) .... I THINK I LOVE YOU

Answers on page 270

MONTH BY MONTH: 2003

All data below refers to positions achieved on the Official Singles Chart or (where relevant) the Official Albums Chart.

JANUARY: Erasure scored their sixteenth Top 10 hit with a cover of *Solsbury Hill* – who first reached the Top 20 with the song in 1977?

FEBRUARY: Rock band Good Charlotte scored their first of five Top 10 hits with which song?

MARCH: Gareth Gates teamed up with The Kumars for Comic Relief and debuted at Number 1 with a cover of the song *Spirit In The Sky* – in what year did Norman Greenbaum originally take the song to the top of the Official Singles Chart?

APRIL: *Clocks* was the fifth consecutive Top 10 hit for which band?

MAY: Lisa Scott-Lee reached the Top 10 with her debut solo song *Lately* – she's also the member of another chart act, but can you name them?

JUNE: *Gay Bar* was the second Top 5 hit in a row for which band?

JULY: The Coral scored their biggest-ever hit on the Official Singles Chart with which Top 5 song?

AUGUST: What colour of *Eyes* were Ultrabeat singing about, according to the title of their Number 2 debut hit?

SEPTEMBER: After originally charting in July, which band topped the Official Albums Chart for a four-week run with their debut *Permission To Land*?

OCTOBER: Fast Food Rockers followed up *Fast Food Song* with a second consecutive Top 10 hit single – name it.

NOVEMBER: *Flip Reverse* reached Number 2 and gave which boyband their fifth Top 10 hit?

DECEMBER: Shane Richie reached Number 2 with his Children In Need charity cover version of the song *I'm Your Man* – in what year did the original version by Wham! top the Official Singles Chart?

TOP 10: 10 MAY 2003

Fill in the blanks from this complete Official Singles Chart Top 10. If the song title is listed, we're looking for the band or artist that's missing. If the band or artist is listed, we're looking for the missing song title.

1. (NEW) TOMCRAFT ....

2. (NEW) CRAIG DAVID & STING ....

3. (NEW) .... THE LONG GOODBYE

4. (1) .... YOU SAID NO

5. (NEW) .... CAN'T NOBODY

6. (2) LISA MAFFIA ....

7. (5) .... IN DA CLUB

8. (6) DMX ....

9. (4) ROOM 5 FEATURING OLIVER CHEATHAM ....

10. (3) .... DON'T LET GO

Answers on page 270

MONTH BY MONTH: 2004

All data below refers to positions achieved on the Official Singles Chart or (where relevant) the Official Albums Chart.

JANUARY: *Milkshake* reached Number 2 on the Official Singles Chart for which singer?

FEBRUARY: The Number 1 song *Take Me To The Clouds Above* by LMC vs U2 featured lyrics taken from a 1986 Top 5 hit by Whitney Houston – name it.

MARCH: The group VS made their chart debut with the song *Love You Like Mad* – one of their members was Marvin Humes, but with which boyband did he later score a string of Top 10 hits?

APRIL: What was the title of the Official Singles Chart debut for Kanye West?

MAY: Who replaced Eamon's potty-mouthed Number 1 song with *F.U.R.B. (F U Right Back)*, which she claimed to be her own response to his track?

JUNE: Which former member of the Spice Girls reached the Top 20 with the solo hit *Crickets Sing For Anamaria*?

JULY: *Flawless (Go To The City)* was a Top 10 song for George Michael that reinterpreted the 2001 hit *Flawless* by which New York group?

AUGUST: The Libertines scored their biggest-ever hit on the Official Singles Chart, reaching Number 2 with which song?

SEPTEMBER: *Real To Me* was a Number 1 song for which former member of Westlife?

OCTOBER: A cover of the song *More, More, More* was a Top 3 hit for Rachel Stevens – who originally took the record into the Top 5 in May 1976?

NOVEMBER: Which 1989 Bobby Brown hit did Britney Spears successfully cover and take into the Top 3?

DECEMBER: Who sang the first line on Band Aid 20's new version of the Number 1 song *Do They Know It's Christmas*?

TOP 10: 17 APRIL 2004

Fill in the blanks from this complete Official Singles Chart Top 10. If the song title is listed, we're looking for the band or artist that's missing. If the band or artist is listed, we're looking for the missing song title.

1. (1) ....   *5 COLOURS IN HER HAIR*

2. (2) USHER FEATURING LIL' JON & LUDACRIS   ....

3. (NEW) THE RASMUS   ....

4. (5) ....   *LEFT OUTSIDE ALONE*

5. (4) DJ CASPER   ....

6. (NEW) SPECIAL D   ....

7. (3) TWISTA   ....

8. (6) ....   *BREATHE EASY*

9. (NEW) NARCOTIC THRUST   ....

10. (NEW) ....   *NAUGHTY GIRL*

Answers on page 270-1

MONTH BY MONTH: 2005

All data below refers to positions achieved on the Official Singles Chart or (where relevant) the Official Albums Chart.

JANUARY: *Wires* was the only Top 10 hit single for which band?

FEBRUARY: *Sometimes You Can't Make It On Your Own* was a Number 1 on the Official Singles Chart for which Irish group?

MARCH: Sunderland-based band The Futureheads scored their only Top 10 hit with a cover of which 1985 Kate Bush song?

APRIL: The song *Shiver* was a Top 10 hit on the Official Singles Chart and came from *Counting Down The Days*, the Number 1 on the Official Albums Chart, by which female star?

MAY: What one-word title gave Oasis their seventh Number 1 hit single?

JUNE: A cover of *Axel F* put Crazy Frog at Number 1 for four weeks – in what year did musician Harold Faltermeyer originally take the instrumental track to Number 2?

JULY: *Crazy Chick* was a Number 2 hit song for which Welsh singer?

AUGUST: James Blunt had the Number 1 single with *You're Beautiful* while he was simultaneously at Number 1 on the Official Albums Chart – name that multi-platinum selling album.

SEPTEMBER: Which former member of boyband Blue scored his first Top 5 solo hit single with *Lay Your Hands*?

OCTOBER: How many *Bicycles* were mentioned in the title of the Top 10 hit by Katie Melua?

NOVEMBER: *Hung Up* was Madonna's eleventh Number 1 single – which 1979 Top 3 hit by ABBA was heavily sampled on the record?

DECEMBER: Who debuted at Number 1 on the Official Singles Chart with their *JCB Song*?

Answers on page 271

158 *THE OFFICIAL CHARTS' MUSIC QUIZ BOOK*

TOP 10: 15 OCTOBER 2005

Fill in the blanks from this complete Official Singles Chart Top 10. If the song title is listed, we're looking for the band or artist that's missing. If the band or artist is listed, we're looking for the missing song title.

1. (1) .... PUSH THE BUTTON

2. (NEW) .... TRIPPING

3. (2) PUSSYCAT DOLLS FEATURING BUSTA RHYMES ....

4. (NEW) .... PRECIOUS

5. (3) .... WE BE BURNIN'

6. (4) KANYE WEST FEATURING JAMIE FOXX ....

7. (NEW) .... TWO MORE YEARS

8. (5) .... SONG 4 LOVERS

9. (NEW) .... GET YOUR NUMBER / SHAKE IT OFF

10. (6) DANIEL POWTER ....

Answers on page 271

All data below refers to positions achieved on the Official Singles Chart or (where relevant) the Official Albums Chart.

JANUARY: *When The Sun Goes Down* was second consecutive Number 1 single for which group?

FEBRUARY: DJ and producer Meck teamed up with Leo Sayer for a dance remix of the song *Thunder In My Heart* and took it all the way to Number 1 – in what year did Leo's original version peak at Number 22?

MARCH: What was the title of Corinne Bailey Rae's biggest hit single that debuted and peaked at Number 2?

APRIL: How many weeks did Gnarls Barkley spend at Number 1 with the song *Crazy*?

MAY: *Steady As She Goes* was a Top 5 hit for The Raconteurs, a spin-off project by musician Jack White – he'd previously appeared on the Official Singles Chart as a core member of which duo?

JUNE: The song *Monster* reached the Top 5 for which Welsh band?

JULY: Which 1979 Top 10 hit by Queen did McFly cover and take to Number 1 as part of a double-A-side single with *Please, Please*?

AUGUST: *You Give Me Something*, the Top 10 hit on the Official Singles Chart, came from the Number 1 on the Official Albums Chart titled *Undiscovered* – name the musician who brought us that song and album.

SEPTEMBER: The song *Never Be Lonely* was the third consecutive Top 10 hit for which band?

OCTOBER: Name the only Top 10 hit on the Official Singles Chart that was credited to the cast of *High School Musical*.

NOVEMBER: *Patience* was the comeback hit that saw which boyband return to Number 1 for the first time since their original split in 1996?

DECEMBER: *You Know My Name* was the theme song from the James Bond movie *Casino Royale*, and it gave Chris Cornell a solo Top 10 hit – with which band was he also the lead singer?

TOP 10: 21 OCTOBER 2006

Fill in the blanks from this complete Official Singles Chart Top 10. If the song title is listed, we're looking for the band or artist that's missing. If the band or artist is listed, we're looking for the missing song title.

1. (NEW) MY CHEMICAL ROMANCE — ....

2. (1) .... — AMERICA

3. (2) .... — I DON'T FEEL LIKE DANCIN'

4. (5) BOB SINCLAR & CUTEE B — ....

5. (4) P DIDDY FEATURING NICOLE SCHERZINGER — ....

6. (8) .... — CHECKIN' IT OUT

7. (43) .... — SUPERFREAK

8. (6) .... — WHEN YOU WERE YOUNG

9. (9) .... — SEXYBACK

10. (3) DAVID HASSELHOFF — ....

Answers on page 271

All data below refers to positions achieved on the Official Singles Chart or (where relevant) the Official Albums Chart.

JANUARY: *Starz In Their Eyes* spent seven weeks inside the Top 10 on the Official Singles Chart for which act?

FEBRUARY: What was the title of the Number 2 song that brought hitmakers Gwen Stefani and Akon together?

MARCH: *Acceptable In The 80s* was the Top 40 hit debut for which musician?

APRIL: What did Natasha Bedingfield say *I Wanna Have,* according to the title of her Top 10 song?

MAY: The Number 2 hit *Your Love Alone Is Not Enough* by Manic Street Preachers featured their singer James Dean Bradfield alongside the frontwoman of the Swedish group The Cardigans – name her.

JUNE: Which former Sugababes member reached Number 2 with the song *Real Girl*?

JULY: Who were The Hoosiers *Worried About* on their Official Singles Chart debut?

AUGUST: Which American rock act has a Top 20 hit with their version of *The Simpsons Theme*?

SEPTEMBER: *Delivery* was the fourth and final Top 10 hit single for Pete Doherty's side-project away from The Libertines – can you name his other group?

OCTOBER: Which legendary Manchester indie band did The Wombats suggest *Let's Dance To* on their Top 20 hit?

NOVEMBER: For how many weeks did Leona Lewis stay at Number 1 on the Official Singles Chart with *Bleeding Love*?

DECEMBER: *X Factor* winner Leon Jackson had the Christmas Number 1 with a cover of the 1998 Top 5 song *When You Believe* – name the two music icons who teamed up on that original hit duet.

TOP 10: 22 SEPTEMBER 2007

Fill in the blanks from this complete Official Singles Chart Top 10. If the song title is listed, we're looking for the band or artist that's missing. If the band or artist is listed, we're looking for the missing song title.

1. (1) SEAN KINGSTON

2. (2) PLAIN WHITE T's

3. (3) .... STRONGER

4. (4) 1973

5. (8) 50 CENT FEATURING JUSTIN TIMBERLAKE AND TIMBALAND

6. (6) .... SHUT UP AND DRIVE

7. (5) .... SEXY! NO, NO, NO...

8. (7) ROBYN FEATURING KLEERUP

9. (10) TIMBERLAND FEATURING D.O.E. AND KERI HILSON

10. (9) .... SHE'S SO LOVELY

Answers on page 271

All data below refers to positions achieved on the Official Singles Chart or (where relevant) the Official Albums Chart.

JANUARY: Adele made her debut on the Official Singles Chart with which song?

FEBRUARY: Who group said they were *Ready For The Floor* on their only Top 10 hit?

MARCH: Duffy was at Number 1 on the Official Singles Chart with *Mercy* while she simultaneously topped the Official Albums Chart – name that multi-platinum-selling debut album.

APRIL: Danish pop band Alphabeat arrived for the first time inside the Top 10 with which song?

MAY: What sort of *Nightmares* were the band Pendulum having, according to the title of their Top 10 hit?

JUNE: Mint Royale's 2005 cover of *Singin' In The Rain* re-entered the Official Singles Chart and shot to Number 1 after it featured in a dance routine by *Britain's Got Talent* winner George Sampson, but which French act had a Top 20 hit with the same song in April 1978?

JULY: The Top 5 hit *Stay With Me* was the chart debut for which MOBO Award-winning musician?

AUGUST: What was the title of the Number 1 song that saw Katy Perry appear on the Official Singles Chart for the very first time?

SEPTEMBER: Which British music legend marked the fiftieth anniversary of his Official Singles Chart debut with his latest Top 3 hit *Thank You For A Lifetime*?

OCTOBER: *The Winner's Song* by Geraldine was a Number 2 hit song – which Bolton comedian co-wrote the parody track with Gary Barlow and played the Geraldine character on TV?

NOVEMBER: What was the title of the Number 1 album by The Killers which featured their Top 3 hit song *Human*?

DECEMBER: Alexandra Burke had the Christmas Number 1 on the Official Singles Chart with her cover of the Leonard Cohen song *Hallelujah* – which acclaimed musician got stuck behind her at Number 2 with yet another version?

TOP 10: 5 JULY 2008

Fill in the blanks from this complete Official Singles Chart Top 10. If the song title is listed, we're looking for the band or artist that's missing. If the band or artist is listed, we're looking for the missing song title.

1. (2) .... **CLOSER**

2. (1) .... **VIVA LA VIDA**

3. (10) JORDIN SPARKS FEATURING CHRIS BROWN ....

4. (5) CHRIS BROWN ....

5. (3) .... **TAKE A BOW**

6. (4) SARA BAREILLES ....

7. (6) .... **SWEET ABOUT ME**

8. (7) .... **THAT'S NOT MY NAME**

9. (9) .... **WARWICK AVENUE**

10. (14) BUSTA RHYMES FEATURING LINKIN PARK ....

Answers on page 272

All data below refers to positions achieved on the Official Singles Chart or (where relevant) the Official Albums Chart.

JANUARY: Lady Gaga made her debut on the Official Singles Chart with a song that featured Colby O'Donis as a credited vocalist – name that Number 1 hit.

FEBRUARY: *The Fear* was the second of three Number 1 songs for Lily Allen – which famous 1990 Number 1 hit did her dad Keith co-write?

MARCH: The Comic Relief Number 1 hit *Barry Islands In The Stream* saw Tom Jones and Robin Gibb team up with Vanessa Jenkins and Bryn West – those two characters were played by Ruth Jones and Rob Brydon in which BBC sitcom?

APRIL: What was La Roux going *In For*, according to the title of her Number 2 debut hit?

MAY: *Fairytale*, the winning song at Eurovision for Alexander Rybak, entered the Top 10 on the Official Singles Chart – what country did Rybak represent at the song contest?

JUNE: With which member of Destiny's Child did David Guetta collaborate on the Number 1 song *When Love Takes Over*?

JULY: *Beat Again* was the debut Number 1 single for which boyband?

AUGUST: Shortly after his premature death at the age of just 50, which pop icon topped the Official Albums Chart for seven consecutive weeks with the compilation titled *The Essential*?

SEPTEMBER: Where in the world did Mini Viva say they'd *Left My Heart*, according to the title of their only Top 10 hit?

OCTOBER: Which American city did Paloma Faith sing about on her second Top 20 hit single that year?

NOVEMBER: After featuring on Flo Rida's Number 1 song in March titled *Right Round,* which singer made her solo Top 5 debut with the hit *TiK ToK?*

DECEMBER: The surprise Christmas Number 1 was *Killing In The Name* by Rage Against The Machine – in what year did the song first appear on the Official Singles Chart?

TOP 10: 17 OCTOBER 2009

Fill in the blanks from this complete Official Singles Chart Top 10. If the song title is listed, we're looking for the band or artist that's missing. If the band or artist is listed, we're looking for the missing song title.

1. (NEW) ....   OOPSY DAISY

2. (NEW) ....   FOREVER IS OVER

3. (2) JAY-Z FEATURING ALICIA KEYS   ....

4. (1) ....   BREAK YOUR HEART

5. (3) DAVID GUETTA FEATURING AKON   ....

6. (7) THE TEMPER TRAP   ....

7. (4) ....   SHE WOLF

8. (5) ....   I GOTTA FEELING

9. (9) ....   HOTEL ROOM SERVICE

10. (6) JAY-Z FEATURING RIHANNA & KANYE WEST   ....

Answers on page 272

LIVING FOR THE CITY

We've named this section after Stevie Wonder's 1974 Motown classic, which reached the Top 20 in February that year.

Twenty of the world's top cities are listed, and all you've got to do is name the band or artist who placed each of them on the Official Singles Chart, with the peak position and year in brackets to guide you further.

1.   *Vienna* [Number 2 in February 1981]

2.   *Long Haired Lover From Liverpool* [Number 1 in December 1972]

3.   *Barcelona* [Number 8 in November 1987]

4.   *Rio* [Number 9 in December 1982]

5.   *The Poor People Of Paris* [Number 1 in April 1956]

6.   *Put Your Hands Up For Detroit* [Number 1 in November 2006]

7.   *San Francisco (Be Sure To Wear Some Flowers In Your Hair)* [Number 1 in August 1967]

8.   *Night Boat To Cairo* [Number 6 in April 1980]

9.   *One Night In Bangkok* [Number 12 in December 1984]

10. *Marrakesh Express* [Number 17 in September 1969]

11. *Tokyo Joe* [Number 15 in June 1977]

12. *Midnight In Moscow* [Number 2 in January 1962]

13. *All The Way From Memphis* [Number 10 in September 1973]

14. *Belfast* [Number 8 in December 1977]

15. *Drowning In Berlin* [Number 9 in February 1982]

16. *Viva Las Vegas* [Number 17 in April 1964]

17. *The Boston Tea Party* [Number 13 in July 1976]

18. *Fairytale Of New York* [Number 2 in December 1987]

19. *Streets Of Philadelphia* [Number 2 in April 1994]

20. *Midnight Train To Georgia* [Number 10 in June 1976]

BURN IT UP

We've named this section after a top tune by The Beatmasters and PP Arnold, which reached Number 13 on the Official Singles Chart in October 1988 – here's a red-hot list of other titles associated with heat and burning that should hopefully fire up your brain as you try to remember who sang each of these 20 songs.

1. *Firestarter* [Number 1 in March 1996]

2. *Girl On Fire* [Number 5 in December 2012]

3. *The Heat Is On* [Number 12 in April 1985]

4. *Great Balls Of Fire* [Number 1 in January 1958]

5. *Burn* [Number 1 in August 2013]

6. *Rooms On Fire* [Number 16 in May 1989]

7. *This Wheel's On Fire* [Number 5 in June 1968]

8. *Some Like It Hot* [Number 14 in March 1985]

9. *The Unforgettable Fire* [Number 6 in May 1985]

10. *House On Fire* [Number 6 in March 2022]

11. *Burning Down The House* [Number 7 in September 1999]

12. *Hot In Herre* [Number 4 in June 2002]

13. *If You Can't Stand The Heat* [Number 10 in January 1983]

14. *I'm On Fire* [Number 4 in September 1975]

15. *Burn Baby Burn* [Number 13 in April 2001]

16. *Fire!* [Number 1 in August 1968]

17. *Babylon's Burning* [Number 7 in July 1979]

18. *Smoke Gets In Your Eyes* [Number 1 in March 1959]

19. *Hot Stuff* [Number 11 in June 1979]

20. *We Didn't Start The Fire* [Number 7 in October 1989]

Answers on page 272-3

REGGAE FOR IT NOW

Let's shine the spotlight on some of the very best vintage reggae crossover songs from the Official Singles Chart.

Identify the 20 acts who brought us these top tunes and give yourself an extra bonus pop point for knowing that the title of this section was also a Number 12 hit in September 1979 for Bill Lovelady.

1. *Uptown Top Ranking* [Number 1 in February 1978]

2. *You Can Get It If You Really Want* [Number 2 in October 1970]

3. *Sideshow* [Number 3 in January 1977]

4. *Silly Games* [Number 2 in July 1979]

5. *Double Barrel* [Number 1 in May 1971]

6. *Help Me Make It Through The Night* [Number 6 in January 1975]

7. *The Liquidator* [Number 9 in November 1969]

8. *Wonderful World, Beautiful People* [Number 6 in November 1969]

9. *Love Of The Common People* [Number 9 in July 1970]

10. *Girlie Girlie* [Number 7 in January 1986]

11. *Police And Thieves* [Number 23 in June 1980]

12. *Suzanne Beware Of The Devil* [Number 14 in October 1972]

13. *Let Your Yeah Be Yeah* [Number 5 in September 1971]

14. *Just Don't Want To Be Lonely* [Number 9 in August 1987]

15. *Amigo* [Number 9 in October 1980]

16. *Money In My Pocket* [Number 14 in March 1979]

17. *Hurt So Good* [Number 4 in May 1975]

18. *OK Fred* [Number 11 in October 1979]

19. *Dat* [Number 6 in March 1976]

20. *Young, Gifted And Black* [Number 5 in April 1970]

BE YOUNG, BE FOOLISH, BE HAPPY

It's a song that was initially a hit on the Official Singles Chart for The Tams in 1970 before then being covered by Sonia in 1991, and it inspired us to search out 20 other happy-themed titles.

Can you name the groups and singers who put smiles on our faces with these tunes?

1. *Happy* [Number 1 in January 2014]

2. *Happy Hour* [Number 3 in June 1986]

3. *Born To Make You Happy* [Number 1 in January 2000]

4. *Happy Ending* [Number 7 in October 2007]

5. *Don't Worry, Be Happy* [Number 2 in October 1988]

6. *Happy Jack* [Number 3 in January 1967]

7. *My Happy Ending* [Number 5 in August 2004]

8. *Happy House* [Number 17 in April 1980]

9. *Oh Happy Day* [Number 2 in June 1969]

10. *If It Makes You Happy* [Number 9 in September 1996]

11. *Everybody's Happy Nowadays* [Number 29 in March 1979]

12. *Happy Together* [Number 12 in April 1967]

13. *Violently Happy* [Number 13 in March 1994]

14. *Are You Getting Enough Of What Makes You Happy?* [Number 17 in August 1980]

15. *Happy Birthday, Sweet Sixteen* [Number 3 in January 1962]

16. *Happy Just To Be With You* [Number 11 in September 1995]

17. *Happy To Be On An Island In The Sun* [Number 5 in December 1975]

18. *I Could Be Happy* [Number 7 in January 1982]

19. *Happy Anniversary* [Number 14 in November 1974]

20. *Happy Talk* [Number 1 in July 1982]

Answers on page 273

CHART DOUBLES

It doesn't happen very often, but when it does, it's a very special event for the bands or artists that manage it. We're talking about the times when you not only have the Number 1 on the Official Singles Chart but simultaneously find yourself sitting at the top of the Official Albums Chart too.

Here are 20 album titles that ruled the roost while the same musicians or groups did 'the double' by also having the Number 1 single.

Name the acts.

1. *Rubber Soul* [December 1965]

2. *Waking Up The Neighbours* [September 1991]

3. *No.6 Collaborations Project* [July 2019]

4. *Zenyatta Mondatta* [October 1980]

5. *Ta-Dah* [September 2006]

6. *Blue Hawaii* [June 1962]

7. *Heavy Is The Head* [January 2020]

8. *Hard Candy* [April 2008]

9. *The Colour Of My Love* [January 1995]

10. *Chocolate Starfish And The Hot Dog Flavored Water* [January 2001]

11. *Bangerz* [August 2013]

12. *Business As Usual* [February 1983]

13. *Good Girl Gone Bad* [June 2007]

14. *Dark Lane Demo Tapes* [May 2020]

15. *In The Lonely Hour* [March 2015]

16. *High On The Happy Side* [February 1992]

17. *Right Place Right Time* [November 2012]

18. *Feels So Good* [September 2002]

19. *Up* [April 1992]

20. *Guilty* [November 1980]

Answers on page 273

HIT AFTER HIT:
ONE DIRECTION

Place these five **ONE DIRECTION** hits in their correct chronological order as they each appeared on the Official Singles Chart.

A. BEST SONG EVER

B. DRAG ME DOWN

C. STEAL MY GIRL

D. STORY OF MY LIFE

E. ONE WAY OR ANOTHER (TEENAGE KICKS)

Answers on page 273

ONE TO FIVE:
GIRLS ALOUD

Each of these **GIRLS ALOUD** hits achieved a different peak position on the Official Singles Chart – put them in the correct order, starting with Number 1 and working your way down to Number 5.

A. THE PROMISE

B. BIOLOGY

C. SEXY! NO, NO, NO...

D. LOVE MACHINE

E. CALL THE SHOTS

Answers on page 273

HIT AFTER HIT:
DEPECHE MODE

Place these eighties hits by **DEPECHE MODE** in their correct chronological order as they appeared on the Official Singles Chart during that decade.

A. SEE YOU

B. PEOPLE ARE PEOPLE

C. MASTER AND SERVANT

D. EVERYTHING COUNTS

E. JUST CAN'T GET ENOUGH

Answers on page 274

ONE TO FIVE:
THE PRODIGY

Each of these **PRODIGY** hits achieved a different peak position on the Official Singles Chart – put them in the correct order, starting with Number 1 and working your way down to Number 5.

A. CHARLY

B. FIRESTARTER

C. OMEN

D. BABY'S GOT A TEMPER

E. EVERYBODY IN THE PLACE (EP)

Answers on page 274

GOING DOWN TO LIVERPOOL

The city is famous around the world for being the birthplace of The Beatles, of course, but they were just a catalyst for a rich and varied selection of Merseyside musicians and performers to follow in their wake. Here are 20 of the very best hits they created.

Can you name the bands and artists that put them on the Official Singles Chart?

1. *Enola Gay* [Number 8 in November 1980]

2. *All Together Now* [Number 4 in December 1990]

3. *Reward* [Number 6 in March 1981]

4. *Wonderful Life* [Number 8 in September 1987]

5. *There She Goes* [Number 13 in November 1990]

6. *The Cutter* [Number 8 in February 1983]

7. *Americanos* [Number 4 in April 1989]

8. *I Turn To You* [Number 1 in August 2000]

9. *The First Picture Of You* [Number 15 in August 1983]

10. *Nothing's Real But Love* [Number 10 in December 2011]

11. *Ideal World* [Number 14 in January 1988]

12. *Wishful Thinking* [Number 9 in January 1984]

13. *Step Inside Love* [Number 8 in April 1968]

14. *Love Is A Wonderful Colour* [Number 15 in January 1984]

15. *Why Won't You Give Me Your Love?* [Number 9 in April 2006]

16. *Sinful* [Number 13 in June 1986]

17. *Driving Away From Home (Jim's Tune)* [Number 18 in April 1986]

18. *In The Morning* [Number 6 in May 2005]

19. *The More You Live, The More You Love* [Number 26 in August 1984]

20. *I'd Rather Jack* [Number 8 in April 1989]

Answers on page 274

SUPERSTAR SPOTLIGHT:
KYLIE MINOGUE

1. Starting with her 1988 debut *I Should Be So Lucky* through to *Shocked* in June 1991, and including her Jason Donovan collaboration *Especially For You*, how many consecutive Top 10 hits did Kylie achieve on the Official Singles Chart?

2. *If You Were With Me Now* reached Number 4 in November 1991 and featured Kylie alongside which American soul singer?

3. Name Kylie's only Number 1 song during the whole of the nineties on the Official Singles Chart.

4. How many of Kylie's songs have got stuck at Number 2 on the Official Singles Chart?

5. Which famous popstar and choreographer, who had a trio of Top 10 hits of her own during the 1980s and 1990s, co-wrote Kylie's Number 1 single *Spinning Around*?

6. Each of these Kylie hits achieved a different peak position on the Official Singles Chart – put them in the correct order, starting with Number 1 and working your way down to Number 5.

    a. *Slow*
    b. *Better The Devil You Know*
    c. *All The Lovers*
    d. *Wow*
    e. *Step Back In Time*

Answers on page 274

FOOTY HITS

Let's be honest, in the first 70 years of the Official Singles Chart, there've been some very questionable songs that have somehow managed to score well, despite featuring tuneless players, supporters and fans from some of biggest football clubs.

We've rounded up 20 of them, so let's see if you can name the people responsible for these often-surprising moments of glory, with each chart peak and year to help you out a bit further.

1. *Three Lions* [Number 1 in June 1996]

2. *Come On You Reds* [Number 1 in May 1994]

3. *Head Over Heels In Love* [Number 31 in June 1979]

4. *We Have A Dream* [Number 5 in May 1982]

5. *Blue Is The Colour* [Number 5 in March 1972]

6. *Here We Go* [Number 14 in May 1985]

7. *Eat My Goal* [Number 19 in May 1998]

8. *Diamond Lights* [Number 12 in May 1987]

9. *Come On England* [Number 2 in June 2004]

10. *Southgate You're The One (Football's Coming Home Again)* [Number 14 in July 2021]

11. *I'm Forever Blowing Bubbles* [Number 31 in May 1975]

12. *Nice One Cyril* [Number 14 in March 1973]

13. *Sven Sven Sven* [Number 7 in October 2001]

14. *Hot Stuff* [Number 9 in May 1998]

15. *We Can Do It* [Number 15 in May 1977]

16. *Bluebirds Flying High* [Number 15 in May 2008]

17. *We've Got The Whole World In Our Hands* [Number 24 in March 1978]

18. *Don't Come Home Too Soon* [Number 15 in June 1998]

19. *We're On The Ball* [Number 3 in June 2002]

20. *Vindaloo* [Number 2 in June 1998]

Answers on page 274

HIT AFTER HIT:
PET SHOP BOYS

Place these five **PET SHOP BOYS** hits in their correct chronological order as they each appeared on the Official Singles Chart.

A. SO HARD

B. SUBURBIA

C. RENT

D. LEFT TO MY OWN DEVICES

E. IT'S A SIN

Answers on page 274

ONE TO FIVE:
McFLY

Each of these **McFLY** hits achieved a different peak position on the Official Singles Chart – put them in the correct order, starting with Number 1 and working your way down to Number 5.

A. ONE FOR THE RADIO

B. LIES

C. OBVIOUSLY

D. ROOM ON THE THIRD FLOOR

E. THAT GIRL

Answers on page 274

LONG HOT SUMMER

Here are 20 great songs that all appeared the Official Singles Chart from the 1950s onwards, each with the word 'summer' in the title.

Identify the acts behind these hit titles.

1.   *In The Summertime* [Number 1 in June 1970]

2.   *The Boys Of Summer* [Number 12 in March 1985]

3.   *All Summer Long* [Number 1 in August 2008]

4.   *Summer Holiday* [Number 1 in March 1963]

5.   *Summertime* [Number 8 in August 1991]

6.   *Here Comes Summer* [Number 1 in October 1959]

7.   *Cool For The Summer* [Number 7 in September 2015]

8.   *The Second Summer Of Love* [Number 23 in July 1989]

9.   *Summerlove Sensation* [Number 3 in August 1974]

10.   *Summer In The City* [Number 8 in August 1966]

11.   *Cruel Summer* [Number 8 in August 1983]

12.   *Summer Breeze* [Number 16 in June 1974]

13.   *Summertime Sadness* [Number 4 in August 2013]

14.   *Rain In The Summertime* [Number 18 in October 1987]

15.   *Summer Nights* [Number 1 in September 1978]

16.   *Staying Out For The Summer '95* [Number 19 in June 1995]

17.   *Farewell My Summer Love* [Number 7 in June 1984]

18.   *Summer (The First Time)* [Number 9 in September 1973]

19.   *Summer Of Love* [Number 8 in July 2000]

20.   *Summer Night City* [Number 5 in October 1978]

Answers on page 274-5

GOING MISSING

As we've already done this with a set of songs from
both the eighties and the nineties, let's do it again,
this time with Top 10 hits from the noughties.

Every word that was originally listed in brackets when these titles
appeared on the Official Singles Chart has been removed.

We've listed the band or artist along with their peak
position and year, so just fill in the blanks.

1. (__ __ __ __ __) Amarillo?
    Tony Christie featuring Peter Kay [Number 1 in March 2005]

2. Single Ladies (__ __ __ __ __)
    Beyoncé [Number 7 in January 2009]

3. The Cheeky Song (__ __ __)
    The Cheeky Girls [Number 2 in December 2002]

4. Groovejet (__ __ __ __)
    Spiller featuring Sophie Ellis-Bextor [Number 1 in August 2000]

5. I Wish I Was A Punk Rocker (__ __ __ __ __)
    Sandi Thom [Number 1 in June 2006]

6. Here (__ __ __)
    Hellogoodbye [Number 4 in June 2007]

7. Don't Be Stupid (__ __ __ __ __)
    Shania Twain [Number 5 in February 2000]

8. The Ketchup Song (__)
    Las Ketchup [Number 1 in October 2002]

9. Shackles (__ __)
    Mary Mary [Number 5 in June 2000]

10. Anyone Of Us (__ __)
    Gareth Gates [Number 1 in July 2002]

11. My Neck My Back (__ __)
    Khia [Number 4 in October 2004]

12. Lady (__ __ __)
    Modjo [Number 1 in September 2000]

13. *Shakepeare's (___ ___) Words*
One True Voice [Number 10 in June 2003]

14. *Big Girl (___ ___ ___)*
Mika [Number 9 in August 2007]

15. *Never Leave You (___ ___ ___ ___)*
Lumidee [Number 2 in August 2003]

16. *Bound 4 Da Reload (___)*
Oxide & Neutrino [Number 1 in May 2000]

17. *Leave (___ ___)*
JoJo [Number 2 in September 2004]

18. *Jai Ho! (___ ___ ___ ___)*
AR Rahman & The Pussycat Dolls featuring Nicole
Scherzinger [Number 3 in April 2009]

19. *Don't Upset The Rhythm (___ ___ ___)*
Noisettes [Number 2 in April 2009]

20. *All Good Things (___ ___ ___ ___)*
Nelly Furtado [Number 4 in December 2006]

Answers on page 275

SUPERSTAR SPOTLIGHT:

1. In what year did Calvin Harris score his debut hit on the Official Singles Chart with the song *Acceptable In The 80s*?

2. Who was Calvin's collaborator on the song *Blame*, which debuted at Number 1 in September 2014?

3. What was the title of Rihanna's Number 1 hit from 2011, produced by Calvin, which spent a total of six weeks at the top of the Official Singles Chart?

4. How many Official Singles Chart Top 10 hits can be found on Calvin's 2012 Number 1 album *18 Months*?

5. Dizzee Rascal and Chrome featured on Calvin's first Number 1, back in 2008 – name that hit.

6. Each of these Calvin hits achieved a different peak position on the Official Singles Chart – put them in the correct order, starting with Number 1 and working your way down to Number 5.

    a. *Ready For The Weekend*
    b. *Feel So Close*
    c. *I'm Not Alone*
    d. *Drinking From The Bottle (featuring Tinie Tempah)*
    e. *My Way*

Answers on page 275

HIT AFTER HIT:
KANYE WEST

Place these five **KANYE WEST** hits in their correct chronological order as they each appeared on the Official Singles Chart.

A. STRONGER

B. LOVE LOCKDOWN

C. HURRICANE

D. DIAMONDS FROM SIERRA LEONE

E. FOLLOW GOD

Answers on page 275

ONE TO FIVE:
JENNIFER LOPEZ

Each of these **JENNIFER LOPEZ** hits achieved a different peak position on the Official Singles Chart – put them in the correct order, starting with Number 1 and working your way down to Number 5.

A. WAITING FOR TONIGHT

B. LOVE DON'T COST A THING

C. ALL I HAVE (FEATURING LL COOL J)

D. JENNY FROM THE BLOCK

E. IF YOU HAD MY LOVE

Answers on page 275

WOMANKIND

Rock band Little Angels used the word as the title for their January 1993 Top 20 hit, and throughout the history of the Official Singles Chart, almost every sort of woman has been celebrated in song.

See if you can name the 20 different bands and musicians who brought us these.

1. *Man! I Feel Like A Woman!* [Number 3 in October 1999]

2. *Devil Woman* [Number 9 in June 1976]

3. *Oh, Pretty Woman* [Number 1 in November 1964]

4. *This Woman's Work* [Number 25 in December 1989]

5. *I Recall A Gypsy Woman* [Number 13 in July 1976]

6. *I'm Not A Girl, Not Yet A Woman* [Number 2 in April 2002]

7. *Boogie On Reggae Woman* [Number 12 in February 1975]

8. *Woman* [Number 13 in October 2021]

9. *When A Woman* [Number 6 in June 2000]

10. *Strange Kind Of Woman* [Number 8 in March 1971]

11. *Woman In Love* [Number 1 in October 1980]

12. *Ain't Gonna Bump No More (With No Big Fat Woman)* [Number 2 in May 1977]

13. *Woman Like Me* [Number 2 in November 2018]

14. *Show Me You're A Woman* [Number 8 in December 1975]

15. *Whole Lotta Woman* [Number 1 in April 1958]

16. *Long Legged Woman Dressed In Black* [Number 13 in May 1974]

17. *Power Of A Woman* [Number 5 in October 1995]

18. *Sweet Talkin' Woman* [Number 6 in October 1978]

19. *God Is A Woman* [Number 4 in July 2018]

20. *Woman In Chains* [Number 26 in December 1989]

BOYS WILL BE BOYS

Let's test your knowledge on some of the great (and admittedly not-so-great) boybands of the nineties and noughties. We've listed 20 of their hits from the Official Singles Chart.

Can you name the pop pinups who brought us these songs?

1. *No Matter What* [Number 1 in August 1998]

2. *All Rise* [Number 4 in June 2001]

3. *Why Can't I Wake Up With You* [Number 2 in February 1993]

4. *Bye Bye Bye* [Number 3 in March 2000]

5. *I've Got A Little Something For You* [Number 2 in March 1995]

6. *Be Alone No More* [Number 6 in February 1998]

7. *Quit Playing Games (With My Heart)* [Number 2 in January 1997]

8. *Change Your Mind* [Number 11 in February 1996]

9. *Year 3000* [Number 2 in January 2003]

10. *More To This World* [Number 8 in May 1994]

11. *Liquid Dreams* [Number 3 in April 2001]

12. *If Ya Gettin' Down* [Number 2 in July 1999]

13. *I'm A Man Not A Boy* [Number 7 in May 1997]

14. *Fool Again* [Number 1 in April 2000]

15. *Hold On Me* [Number 10 in November 2003]

16. *I Wanna Sex You Up* [Number 1 in June 1991]

17. *Forever* [Number 6 in December 1996]

18. *Same Old Brand New You* [Number 1 in November 2000]

19. *Step By Step* [Number 2 in June 1990]

20. *Deep* [Number 5 in February 1993]

Answers on page 275

HIT AFTER HIT:
EAST 17

Place these nineties hits by **EAST 17** in their correct chronological order as they appeared on the Official Singles Chart during that decade.

A. THUNDER

B. HOUSE OF LOVE

C. STAY ANOTHER DAY

D. STEAM

E. IT'S ALRIGHT

Answers on page 275

ONE TO FIVE:
911

Each of these **911** hits achieved a different peak position on the Official Singles Chart – put them in the correct order, starting with Number 1 and working your way down to Number 5.

A. A LITTLE BIT MORE

B. BODYSHAKIN'

C. PARTY PEOPLE … FRIDAY NIGHT

D. THE DAY WE FIND LOVE

E. MORE THAN A WOMAN

Answers on page 275

TELL ME WHEN

It can be an adverb, a conjunction, a noun, or a pronoun. 'When' is a very useful word in grammar, and it's often been the starting point for so many titles on the Official Singles Chart.

Can you name the musicians and performers of these songs?

1. *When You Say Nothing At All* [Number 1 in August 1999]

2. *When A Child Is Born (Soleado)* [Number 1 in December 1976]

3. *When Smokey Sings* [Number 11 in July 1987]

4. *When Love Breaks Down* [Number 25 in November 1985]

5. *When I Think Of You* [Number 10 in September 1986]

6. *When The Sun Goes Down* [Number 1 in January 2006]

7. *When I Was Your Man* [Number 2 in March 2013]

8. *When Christmas Comes Around* [Number 3 in December 2016]

9. *When Forever Has Gone* [Number 2 in October 1976]

10. *When I Grow Up* [Number 3 in September 2008]

11. *When You're Young And In Love* [Number 13 in July 1967]

12. *When She Was My Girl* [Number 3 in November 1981]

13. *When I'm Good And Ready* [Number 5 in April 1993]

14. *When I Need You* [Number 1 in February 1977]

15. *When The Heartache Is Over* [Number 10 in October 1999]

16. *When You Come Back To Me* [Number 2 in January 1990]

17. *When We Were Young* [Number 10 in June 1983]

18. *When You Are A King* [Number 13 in July 1971]

19. *When You Tell Me That You Love Me* [Number 2 in December 1991]

20. *When Love Takes Over* [Number 1 in June 2009]

Answers on page 276

REGAL HITS

King Charles III's accession to the throne in September 2022 inspired this next section of quiz questions.

Here are 20 examples of royalty and nobility being referenced in song titles, so which bands and artists took each of them onto the Official Singles Chart?

1. *Killer Queen* [Number 2 in November 1974]

2. *Prince Charming* [Number 1 in September 1981]

3. *Sir Duke* [Number 2 in May 1977]

4. *The King Of Rock 'N' Roll* [Number 7 in May 1988]

5. *Dancing Queen* [Number 1 in September 1976]

6. *King* [Number 1 in March 2015]

7. *Two Princes* [Number 3 in June 1993]

8. *Trap Queen* [Number 8 in June 2015]

9. *King Creole* [Number 2 in October 1958]

10. *The Prince* [Number 16 in October 1979]

11. *Queen Of Clubs* [Number 7 in September 1974]

12. *King Of The Road* [Number 1 in May 1965]

13. *Duke Of Earl* [Number 6 in August 1979]

14. *Queen Of My Heart* [Number 1 in November 2001]

15. *Duchess* [Number 14 in September 1979]

16. *King In A Catholic Style (Wake Up)* [Number 19 in June 1985]

17. *Queen Of Hearts* [Number 11 in October 1979]

18. *The Joker And The Queen* [Number 2 in February 2022]

19. *King Of My Castle* [Number 1 in November 1999]

20. *God Save The Queen* [Number 2 in June 1977]

Answers on page 276

HIT AFTER HIT:
BROS

Place these eighties hits by **BROS** in their correct chronological order as they appeared on the Official Singles Chart during that decade.

A.	I QUIT
B.	DROP THE BOY
C.	TOO MUCH
D.	CAT AMONG THE PIGEONS
E.	I OWE YOU NOTHING

Answers on page 276

ONE TO FIVE:
THE SATURDAYS

Each of these hits by **THE SATURDAYS** achieved a different peak position on the Official Singles Chart – put them in the correct order, starting with Number 1 and working your way down to Number 5.

A.	JUST CAN'T GET ENOUGH
B.	MISSING YOU
C.	WHAT ABOUT US (FEATURING SEAN PAUL)
D.	UP
E.	ISSUES

Answers on page 276

OUT OF THIS WORLD

We're heading off into the galaxy for 20 space-related songs. You've just got to name the acts who brought them into the Official Singles Chart in its first 70 years. Oh, and one of the songs on this list is so old that it reached Number 1 a whole 15 years before Neil Armstrong even set foot on the moon!

1. *Space Man* [Number 2 in May 2022]

2. *Planet Earth* [Number 12 in March 1981]

3. *Starships* [Number 2 in March 2012]

4. *To The Moon And Back* [Number 3 in August 1998]

5. *Calling Occupants Of Interplanetary Craft* [Number 9 in November 1977]

6. *Kelly Watch The Stars* [Number 18 in May 1998]

7. *Drops Of Jupiter (Tell Me)* [Number 10 in August 2001]

8. *The Space Jungle* [Number 7 in September 1990]

9. *Clouds Across The Moon* [Number 6 in April 1985]

10. *Walking On The Milky Way* [Number 17 in August 1996]

11. *Astronaut In The Ocean* [Number 12 in June 2021]

12. *Girl From Mars* [Number 11 in August 1995]

13. *Lost Stars* [Number 6 in April 2015]

14. *Saturn 5* [Number 20 in January 1994]

15. *I See The Moon* [Number 1 in March 1954]

16. *Intergalactic* [Number 5 in July 1998]

17. *I Lost My Heart To A Starship Trooper* [Number 6 in December 1978]

18. *Space Cowboy* [Number 17 in October 1994]

19. *Kiss The Stars* [Number 8 in January 2012]

20. *Spaceman* [Number 1 in January 1996]

Answers on page 276

LOOK WHAT YOU MADE ME DO

Look at all these hits with the word 'look' in the title.

See if you can correctly name the performers who brought each of them to the Official Singles Chart.

1.   *The Look Of Love* [Number 4 in June 1982]

2.   *I Bet You Look Good On The Dancefloor*
     [Number 1 in October 2005]

3.   *U Got The Look* [Number 11 in September 1987]

4.   *Fix Up Look Sharp* [Number 17 in August 2003]

5.   *The Look* [Number 7 in May 1989]

6.   *Look Through Any Window* [Number 4 in September 1965]

7.   *Don't Look Back Into The Sun* [Number 11 in August 2003]

8.   *Look Wot You Dun* [Number 4 in February 1972]

9.   *Don't Look Down – The Sequel* [Number 13 in December 1985]

10. Look Right Through [Number 1 in November 2013]

11. *Stop Look Listen (To Your Heart)* [Number 25 in August 1974]

12. *Look At Me* [Number 2 in May 1999]

13. *Look Mama* [Number 10 in April 1985]

14. *Take A Look Around* [Number 13 in May 1972]

15. *Won't Look Back* [Number 2 in September 2014]

16. *Looking Through The Eyes Of Love* [Number 3 in July 1965]

17. *That Look In Your Eye* [Number 5 in May 1995]

18. *Look Away* [Number 7 in April 1986]

19. *When You Look At Me* [Number 3 in June 2002]

20. *Don't Look Any Further* [Number 9 in December 1993]

Answers on page 276-7

SUPERSTAR SPOTLIGHT:
MADONNA

1. Name Madonna's first Official Singles Chart Number 1.

2. Madonna's first greatest hits album was released in November 1990, and it's ranked as one of the UK's 20 all-time best-sellers – what is its title?

3. What's the four-letter title of her 2012 studio album, which debuted at Number 1 on the Official Albums Chart?

4. Madonna was the guest featured vocalist on a Number 2 song for Britney Spears in November 2003 – what was the title of that hit?

5. In April 1990, *Vogue* became Madonna's seventh Number 1 hit, but in what year did she achieve her eighth on the Official Singles Chart with the song *Frozen*?

6. Each of these Madonna hits achieved a different peak position on the Official Singles Chart – put them in the correct order, starting with Number 1 and working your way down to Number 10.

   a. *Deeper And Deeper*
   b. *Erotica*
   c. *You Must Love Me*
   d. *Ray Of Light*
   e. *La Isla Bonita*
   f. *Human Nature*
   g. *Jump*
   h. *Dress You Up*
   i. *Don't Tell Me*
   j. *What It Feels Like For A Girl*

Answers on page 277

TURN BACK THE CLOCK

Next, here are 20 songs on the theme of 'time'.

All you've got to do is figure out which bands and artists put each of them onto the Official Singles Chart – your time starts NOW!

1. *One Moment In Time* [Number 1 in October 1988]

2. *If I Could Turn Back Time* [Number 6 in October 1989]

3. *The Time Is Now* [Number 2 in April 2000]

4. *My Favourite Waste Of Time* [Number 3 in July 1986]

5. *5 Years Time* [Number 7 in August 2008]

6. *Marguerita Time* [Number 3 in January 1984]

7. *No Time To Die* [Number 1 in February 2020]

8. *Time Is Tight* [Number 4 in June 1969]

9. *Until The End Of Time* [Number 4 in June 2001]

10. *Now Is The Time* [Number 5 in August 1976]

11. *Twilight Time* [Number 3 in July 1958]

12. *This Is The Right Time* [Number 13 in August 1989]

13. *Step Back In Time* [Number 4 in November 1990]

14. *High Time* [Number 4 in November 1966]

15. *Time To Burn* [Number 3 in August 2000]

16. *Praying For Time* [Number 6 in September 1990]

17. *About Damn Time* [Number 3 in June 2022]

18. *A Question Of Time* [Number 17 in August 1986]

19. *Time Is Running Out* [Number 8 in September 2003]

20. *This Is The Last Time* [Number 18 in December 2004]

SPOTLIGHT:
2010s

MONTH BY MONTH: 2010

All data below refers to positions achieved on the Official Singles Chart or (where relevant) the Official Albums Chart.

JANUARY: Who took the song *Fireflies* to Number 1 on the Official Singles Chart?

FEBRUARY: The Number 2 hit *Under Pressure (Ice Ice Baby)* was a new mash-up of two previous Number 1 hits – it featured Vanilla Ice alongside which famous *X Factor* duo?

MARCH: Tinie Tempah made his Official Singles Chart debut at Number 1 with which song?

APRIL: Name the band who spent two weeks at Number 1 with *This Ain't A Love Song*.

MAY: Two different versions of Billy Joel's *She's Always A Woman* both appeared inside the Top 30 after the song featured in a John Lewis TV ad – Billy's original was one, but who did the new cover version that reached Number 7?

JUNE: The Number 1 by Shout For England, featuring Dizzee Rascal and James Corden, was a new version of the song *Shout*, originally a Top 5 hit in 1984 for which band?

JULY: Professor Green and Lily Allen's Top 5 hit *Just Be Good To Green* was a reworking of the Number 1 song *Dub Be Good To Me* – which group spent four weeks at the top with that track in 1990?

AUGUST: Roll Deep followed up *Good Times* and scored their second consecutive Number 1 hit single of 2010 with which song?

SEPTEMBER: *Crossfire* was the debut solo Top 10 hit on the Official Singles Chart for the frontman of The Killers – name him.

OCTOBER: Duck Sauce entered the Top 3 with the dance smash titled *Barbra Streisand*, but which 1979 Top 20 hit by Boney M was sampled on the track?

NOVEMBER: *The Flood* was a Number 2 hit single for which group?

DECEMBER: Matt Cardle's Christmas Number 1 song *When We Collide* was a cover of a Biffy Clyro hit that reached the Top 20 in January that same year, but with a different three-word title – can you name it?

TOP 10: 14 AUGUST 2010

Fill in the blanks from this complete Official Singles Chart Top 10. If the song title is listed, we're looking for the band or artist that's missing. If the band or artist is listed, we're looking for the missing song title.

1. (NEW) .... **BEAUTIFUL MONSTER**

2. (5) FLO RIDA FEATURING DAVID GUETTA ....

3. (2) YOLANDA BE COOL & DCUP ....

4. (4) EMINEM FEATURING RIHANNA ....

5. (1) .... **ALL TIME LOW**

6. (3) TRAVIE McCOY FEATURING BRUNO MARS ....

7. (6) B.O.B FEATURING HAYLEY WILLIAMS ....

8. (8) .... **PACK UP**

9. (7) SWEDISH HOUSE MAFIA FEATURING PHARRELL ....

10. (9) KATY PERRY FEATURING SNOOP DOGG ....

Answers on page 277

MONTH BY MONTH: 2011

All data below refers to positions achieved on the Official Singles Chart or (where relevant) the Official Albums Chart.

JANUARY: Adele's first single from her record-breaking album *21* made its debut at Number 2 on the Official Singles Chart – what was the title of that song?

FEBRUARY: Name the US R&B star who had his own Top 10 song with *Yeah 3x* while simultaneously appearing as the featured vocalist on Chipmunk's Number 2 hit *Champion*.

MARCH: *Don't Hold Your Breath* was a Number 1 single for which member of the Pussycat Dolls?

APRIL: Tracy Chapman's song *Fast Car* shot to Number 4 after *Britain's Got Talent* contestant Michael Collings performed it on the primetime TV show – in what year did Tracy's original single first reach the Top 5?

MAY: What was Lady Gaga on *The Edge Of*, according to the title of her Top 10 hit?

JUNE: Ed Sheeran made his Official Singles Chart debut at Number 3 with which song?

JULY: The album *4* spent a fortnight at Number 1 on the Official Albums Chart for which superstar?

AUGUST: *Swagger Jagger* was a Number 1 hit song for which former *X Factor* contestant?

SEPTEMBER: Olly Murs teamed up with which duo on the Number 1 single *Heart Skips A Beat*?

OCTOBER: *Video Games* was the debut Top 10 hit song for which singer?

NOVEMBER: After scoring a Number 1 with *What Makes You Beautiful*, what was the title of One Direction's Top 3 follow-up hit?

DECEMBER: Radio 1's *Breakfast Show* host Chris Moyles championed an obscure seasonal song titled *Dominick The Donkey (The Italian Xmas Donkey)* in the race for the Official Singles Chart Christmas Number 1 – it peaked at Number 3, but who was the performer?

THE OFFICIAL CHARTS' *MUSIC QUIZ BOOK*

198

Answers on page 277

TOP 10: 18 JUNE 2011

Fill in the blanks from this complete Official Singles Chart Top 10. If the song title is listed, we're looking for the band or artist that's missing. If the band or artist is listed, we're looking for the missing song title.

1. (NEW) .... *CHANGED THE WAY YOU KISS ME*

2. (1) PITBULL FEATURING NAYER, AFROJACK AND NE-YO

3. (14) NICOLE SCHERZINGER FEATURING 50 CENT

4. (3) .... *MR SAXOBEAT*

5. (2) .... *I NEED A DOLLAR*

6. (NEW) .... *EVERY TEARDROP IS A WATERFALL*

7. (4) LMFAO FEATURING LAUREN BENNETT & GOONROCK

8. (5) .... *THE LAZY SONG*

9. (10) JENNIFER LOPEZ FEATURING LIL WAYNE

10. (12) DEV FEATURING THE CATARACS

Answers on page 277-8

MONTH BY MONTH: 2012

All data below refers to positions achieved on the Official
Singles Chart or (where relevant) the Official Albums Chart.

JANUARY: Who spent two weeks at Number 1 with the song *Domino*?

FEBRUARY: A four-piece band from Barbados called Cover
Drive followed up their debut Top 10 hit *Lick Ya Down* with
an Official Singles Chart Number 1 – what was its title?

MARCH: Which legendary guitarist did Dappy from N-Dubz team up
with on the track *Rockstar* and take the song all the way to Number 2?

APRIL: Carly Rae Jepsen's debut hit spent four
weeks at Number 1 – name that song.

MAY: Which American group made their last ever appearance on the
Official Singles Chart with their tenth Top 20 hit, *Only The Horses?*

JUNE: Girl-group Stooshe scored their biggest
of four Top 40 hits with which song?

JULY: Which rapper was the credited featured artist
alongside Maroon 5 on the Number 1 song *Payphone*?

AUGUST: After featuring prominently during the closing
ceremony of the London 2012 Olympics, which 2008 Elbow
song re-entered the Official Singles Chart at Number 4?

SEPTEMBER: The Number 1 song *Bom Bom*
was the only hit single for which group?

OCTOBER: Adele reached Number 2 with her title
theme song to which blockbuster movie?

NOVEMBER: What sort of *Girl* were JLS singing
about on their Top 10 hit single?

DECEMBER: The Justice Collective scored the Christmas Number 1
with a charity cover of *He Ain't Heavy, He's My Brother* – in what year did
The Hollies take the song to Number 1 on the Official Singles Chart?

TOP 10: 24 NOVEMBER 2012

Fill in the blanks from this complete Official Singles Chart Top 10. If the song title is listed, we're looking for the band or artist that's missing. If the band or artist is listed, we're looking for the missing song title.

1. (NEW) .... LITTLE THINGS

2. (NEW) .... LOCKED OUT OF HEAVEN

3. (NEW) .... DNA

4. (2) LABRINTH FEATURING EMELI SANDÉ ....

5. (36) .... THE POWER OF LOVE

6. (1) .... CANDY

7. (6) .... GANGNAM STYLE

8. (15) THE LUMINEERS ....

9. (8) .... DIAMONDS

10. (NEW) .... LOVE IS EASY

Answers on page 278

All data below refers to positions achieved on the Official Singles Chart or (where relevant) the Official Albums Chart.

JANUARY: James Arthur was back at Number 1 for a second two-week run with the song *Impossible* – it was a cover of a Top 10 hit from 2010 by which Barbadian singer?

FEBRUARY: What sort of *Shop* did Macklemore, Ryan Lewis and Wanz sing about on their Number 1 hit?

MARCH: *Pompeii* was a Number 2 hit on the Official Singles Chart for which group?

APRIL: After performing *Let's Get Ready To Rhumble* on ITV's primetime show *Saturday Night Takeaway*, Ant & Dec landed a surprise Number 1 hit a week later – in what year did the duo first take the song into the Top 10 as PJ & Duncan?

MAY: Daft Punk featuring Pharrell Williams spent four weeks at Number 1 with which song?

JUNE: Which British rock legends went to Number 1 on the Official Albums Chart with their final studio album, titled *13*?

JULY: *Here's To Never Growing Up* was a Top 20 hit on the Official Singles Chart for which Canadian solo star?

AUGUST: Who landed their first ever Number 1 hit with the song *We Can't Stop*?

SEPTEMBER: What one-word title did Katy Perry take to Number 1 on the Official Singles Chart for two weeks?

OCTOBER: Who were *Counting Stars*, according to the title of their Number 1 song?

NOVEMBER: Lily Allen took a cover of Keane's song *Somewhere Only We Know* to Number 1 on the Official Singles Chart after it featured in that year's John Lewis Christmas ad – in what year did Keane's original version first appear inside the Top 3?

DECEMBER: The *X Factor* winner Sam Bailey scored the Christmas Number 1 with a cover of *Skyscraper* – which singer had the original Top 10 hit with the same song in 2012?

TOP 10: 27 JULY 2013

Fill in the blanks from this complete Official Singles Chart Top 10. If the song title is listed, we're looking for the band or artist that's missing. If the band or artist is listed, we're looking for the missing song title.

1. (NEW) .... *WAKE ME UP*

2. (1) ROBIN THICKE FEATURING T.I. AND PHARRELL

3. (2) .... *LOVE ME AGAIN*

4. (4) ICONA POP FEATURING CHARLI XCX

5. (5) .... *BANG BANG*

6. (7) NAUGHTY BOY FEATURING SAM SMITH

7. (3) SEBASTIAN INGROSSO & TOMMY TRASH FEATURING JOHN MARTIN

8. (NEW) .... *COME & GET IT*

9. (NEW) BREACH

10. (8) PASSENGER

Answers on page 278

MONTH BY MONTH: 2014

All data below refers to positions achieved on the Official Singles Chart or (where relevant) the Official Albums Chart.

JANUARY: Who was the credited featured vocalist on Pitbull's Number 1 song *Timber*?

FEBRUARY: DJ and Music producer Zedd teamed up with Hayley Williams for the Number 2 hit *Stay The Night* – with which band has Hayley had success on both the Official Singles and Albums Chart as their lead singer?

MARCH: Name the American duo who had a Top 5 hit when they collaborated with Christina Aguilera for the song *Say Something*.

APRIL: The love song *All Of Me* reached Number 2 and went on to sell more than a million copies for which musician?

MAY: A week after Conchita Wurst won the 2014 Eurovision Song Contest, the song became a Top 20 hit on the Official Singles Chart – name it.

JUNE: A viral campaign to get the track *Noble England* to Number 1 during the 2014 World Cup saw it eventually debut at Number 7 – the performer was an award-winning comedy actor who'd died on the ninth June – who was he?

JULY: The band Rixton made their Official Singles Chart debut in spectacular fashion with a Number 1 hit – what was the five-word title?

AUGUST: Name the Norwegian duo who spent a fortnight at Number 1 with the song *Am I Wrong*?

SEPTEMBER: Drum & bass production duo Sigma scored a Number 1 hit with the track *Changing* – which singer was the featured credited guest vocalist on the song?

OCTOBER: Meghan Trainor spent four weeks at Number 1 with her debut hit single – name it.

NOVEMBER: A fourth version of the Band Aid song *Do They Know It's Christmas* reached Number 1 on the Official Singles Chart – in what year did the second version of the famous charity single top the chart, produced by Stock, Aitken & Waterman?

DECEMBER: Ben Haenow won ITV's talent show the *X Factor* and scored the Christmas Number 1 single – what was the title of his song?

TOP 10: 9 AUGUST 2014

Fill in the blanks from this complete Official Singles Chart Top 10. If the song title is listed, we're looking for the band or artist that's missing. If the band or artist is listed, we're looking for the missing song title.

1. (2) MAGIC!

2. (1) CHERYL COLE FEATURING TINIE TEMPAH

3. (NEW) ZHU

4. (3) .... *GHOST*

5. (NEW) BARS & MELODY

6. (4) .... *BUDAPEST*

7. (5) ARIANA GRANDE FEATURING IGGY AZALEA

8. (6) .... *BOOM CLAP*

9. (7) WILL.I.AM FEATURING CODY WISE

10. (NEW) MELISSA STEEL FEATURING POPCAAN

Answers on page 278

MONTH BY MONTH: 2015

All data below refers to positions achieved on the Official Singles Chart or (where relevant) the Official Albums Chart.

JANUARY: After initially reaching the top just before Christmas 2014, Mark Ronson and Bruno Mars returned to Number 1 for a six-week run on the Official Singles Chart with which song?

FEBRUARY: Which Irish singer said *Take Me To Church* on his Number 2 hit?

MARCH: *Hold Back The River* was a Top 10 hit for which hat-wearing musician?

APRIL: Jess Glynne scored her first Official Singles Chart Number 1 as a solo artist in her own right – what was the three-word title of her hit?

MAY: *Bills* was a Number 2 hit and the only chart entry to date for which American musician?

JUNE: What did the band Walk The Moon tell us to do on the title of their Top 5 hit?

JULY: Who asked *Are You With Me* on their Official Singles Chart Number 1 song?

AUGUST: Following her death on 1 August at the age of 72, which Liverpool legend scored a posthumous Number 1 on the Official Albums Chart with her *Very Best Of* collection?

SEPTEMBER: *Ain't Nobody (Loves Me Better)* by German music producer Felix Jähn featuring teenage singer Jasmine Thompson was a Number 2 hit that re-worked the original chart smash from Rufus & Chaka Khan – in what year did Chaka's version first appear in the Top 10?

OCTOBER: Ed Sheeran signed a singer-songwriter to his Gingerbread Man record label and the move catapulted that musician's song *Wasn't Expecting That* into the Top 10 – what was his name?

NOVEMBER: *Sax* was a Top 3 hit single for which former *X Factor* contestant?

DECEMBER: Which NHS choir had the Christmas Number 1 on the Official Singles Chart with the charity hit *A Bridge Over You*?

Answers on page 278-9

TOP 10: 15 OCTOBER 2015

Fill in the blanks from this complete Official Singles Chart Top 10. If the song title is listed, we're looking for the band or artist that's missing. If the band or artist is listed, we're looking for the missing song title.

1. (2) .... — WHAT DO YOU MEAN

2. (3) R CITY FEATURING ADAM LEVINE — ....

3. (1) .... — WRITING'S ON THE WALL

4. (NEW) PHILIP GEORGE & ANTON POWERS — ....

5. (6) .... — ON MY MIND

6. (9) NAUGHTY BOY FEATURING BEYONCÉ & ARROW BENJAMIN — ....

7. (4) .... — EASY LOVE

8. (17) .... — HOTLINE BLING

9. (7) CALVIN HARRIS & DISCIPLES — ....

10. (8) PIA MIA FEATURING CHRIS BROWN & TYGA — ....

Answers on page 279

All data below refers to positions achieved on the Official Singles Chart or (where relevant) the Official Albums Chart.

JANUARY: Who took the song *Stitches* to Number 1 on the Official Singles Chart?

FEBRUARY: How many *Years* did the band Lukas Graham mention in the title of their Number 1 hit?

MARCH: According to the title of his Number 1 song, where did Mike Posner claim he *Took A Pill*?

APRIL: After teaming up with MNEK on the 2015 Top 5 hit *Never Forget You*, what was the two-word title of Zara Larsson's first solo hit single?

MAY: The Dreamworks animated film *Trolls* provided which artist with the Number 2 hit titled *Can't Stop The Feeling*?

JUNE: Name the 2015 *X Factor* winner who was the credited featured guest artist on *Tears*, a Top 5 hit song for Clean Bandit.

JULY: Two simultaneous Top 5 hits featured the same guest vocalist – *Too Good* by Drake and *This Is What You Came For* by Calvin Harris – so who was the collaborator on both songs?

AUGUST: Calum Scott took a cover version of the song *Dancing On My Own* to Number 2, six years after the original was a Top 10 hit for which Swedish musician?

SEPTEMBER: The song *Heathens* reached the Top 5 on the Official Singles Chart for which award-winning rock duo?

OCTOBER: What was the title of the Top 10 debut solo hit for former One Direction member Niall Horan?

NOVEMBER: Which legendary band are mentioned in the title of the Number 2 hit by Rae Sremmurd featuring Gucci Mane?

DECEMBER: The *X Factor* winner Matt Terry scored a Top 3 debut on the Official Singles Chart with a song written by Ed Sheeran and Amy Wadge – what was its festive title?

TOP 10: 27 OCTOBER 2016

Fill in the blanks from this complete Official Singles Chart Top 10. If the song title is listed, we're looking for the band or artist that's missing. If the band or artist is listed, we're looking for the missing song title.

1. (NEW) .... — *SHOUT OUT TO MY EX*

2. (1) .... — *SAY YOU WON'T LET GO*

3. (2) CHAINSMOKERS FEATURING HALSEY — ....

4. (3) .... — *STARBOY*

5. (17) HAILEE STEINFELD & GREY FEATURING ZEDD — ....

6. (5) SIA FEATURING KENDRICK LAMAR — ....

7. (4) .... — *SIDE TO SIDE*

8. (6) .... — *MY WAY*

9. (7) DJ SNAKE FEATURING JUSTIN BIEBER — ....

10. (9) .... — *24K MAGIC*

Answers on page 279

MONTH BY MONTH: 2017

All data below refers to positions achieved on the Official Singles Chart or (where relevant) the Official Albums Chart.

JANUARY: The Number 2 hit *Human* was the Official Singles Chart debut for which performer?

FEBRUARY: Which rapper had a Top 10 hit with the track *Big For Your Boots*?

MARCH: What were Katy Perry and Skip Marley *Chained To*, according to the title of the Top 5 collaboration?

APRIL: After an unbroken run of 13 weeks at Number 1, who briefly knocked Ed Sheeran's *Shape Of You* off the top of the Official Singles Chart with his debut solo single before Ed then deposed him a week later?

MAY: Name all three credited artists on the Number 1 hit remix version of *Despacito*.

JUNE: The Number 1 charity single by Artists For Grenfell was a cover of *Bridge Over Troubled Water* – in what year did Simon & Garfunkel's original version spend three weeks at the top of the Official Singles Chart?

JULY: What sort of *Thoughts* were DJ Khaled featuring Rihanna & Bryson Tiller having on their Number 1 song?

AUGUST: Dua Lipa scored her first Number 1 on the Official Singles Chart with which song?

SEPTEMBER: The Top 5 hit *Reggaeton Lento (Remix)* was the only chart collaboration between Little Mix and which Latin American boyband?

OCTOBER: *Little Bit Leave It* by Chris & Kem was a Top 20 song shortly after the pair became friends on which primetime ITV2 reality show?

NOVEMBER: The comedy rap track *Man's Not Hot* climbed into the Top 10 and became the debut hit single for which performer?

DECEMBER: The Number 2 song on the Official Singles Chart at Christmas was *River* – it was taken from *Revival*, the Number 1 on the Official Albums Chart by which rap superstar?

Answers on page 279

TOP 10: 9 NOVEMBER 2017

Fill in the blanks from this complete Official Singles Chart Top 10. If the song title is listed, we're looking for the band or artist that's missing. If the band or artist is listed, we're looking for the missing song title.

1. (2) CAMILA CABELLO FEATURING YOUNG THUG ....

2. (1) POST MALONE FEATURING 21 SAVAGE ....

3. (3) MARSHMELLO FEATURING KHALID ....

4. (4) AVICII FEATURING RITA ORA ....

5. (6) ZAYN FEATURING SIA ....

6. (7) .... *PERFECT*

7. (5) .... *TOO GOOD AT GOODBYES*

8. (8) MABEL FEATURING KOJO FUNDS ....

9. (17) .... *HOW LONG*

10. (10) J BALVIN & WILLY WILLIAM ....

Answers on page 279

MONTH BY MONTH: 2018

All data below refers to positions achieved on the Official Singles Chart or (where relevant) the Official Albums Chart.

JANUARY: Who was *Barking*, according to the title of their Number 2 hit?

FEBRUARY: *God's Plan* by Drake started its long run at Number 1 – how many consecutive weeks did it spend at the top of the Official Singles Chart?

MARCH: What was the title of the only Top 3 hit to date for Portugal. The Man?

APRIL: While Keala Settle was sitting in the Top 3 on the Official Singles Chart with the song *This Is Me*, its parent soundtrack album notched up its twelfth week of a whopping 27 at Number 1 on the Official Albums Chart – name the film.

MAY: *This Is America* was a Top 10 hit for the American actor and musician Donald Glover under his rap alias – what is his rapper stage name?

JUNE: The song *Youngblood* started an 18-week run inside the Top 40 on the Official Singles Chart for which band?

JULY: At the height of World Cup mania, *Three Lions* shot back to Number 1 for Baddiel, Skinner & The Lightning Seeds, but in what year did the song first appear on the Top 40 in its original form?

AUGUST: The Canadian duo Loud Luxury teamed up with American singer Brando and scored a Top 10 hit song – what was its one-word title?

SEPTEMBER: *Girls Like You* was a Top 10 hit collaboration between the band Maroon 5 and another Official Singles Chart star – name her.

OCTOBER: *Electricity* was a Top 5 hit song for Mark Ronson and Diplo featuring Dua Lipa – what group alias did the two men use on the track?

NOVEMBER: Name the actor who was Lady Gaga's duet partner on the Official Singles Chart Number 1 song *Shallow*, which also featured on the Official Albums Chart Number 1 original soundtrack to the film *A Star Is Born*.

DECEMBER: LadBaby's first Christmas Number 1 hit was a sausage-roll-themed reworking of Starship's song *We Built This City* – in what year did that original version first reach the Top 40?

Answers on page 279-80

TOP 10: 5 JULY 2018

Fill in the blanks from this complete Official Singles Chart Top 10. If the song title is listed, we're looking for the band or artist that's missing. If the band or artist is listed, we're looking for the missing song title.

1. (2) .... *SHOTGUN*

2. (1) CLEAN BANDIT FEATURING DEMI LOVATO ....

3. (3) *2002*

4. (4) .... *I'LL BE THERE*

5. (11) XXTENTACION ....

6. (8) .... *IF YOU'RE OVER ME*

7. (6) .... *BETTER NOW*

8. (9) CARDI B FEATURING BAD BUNNY & J BALVIN ....

9. (7) .... *LEAVE A LIGHT ON*

10. (10) .... *ONE KISS*

Answers on page 280

MONTH BY MONTH: 2019

All data below refers to positions achieved on the Official Singles Chart or (where relevant) the Official Albums Chart.

JANUARY: Who described someone as being *Sweet But Psycho* during her four-week run at Number 1 with the song?

FEBRUARY: Name the Ariana Grande song that debuted on the Official Singles Chart at Number 1, briefly replacing her other hit, *7 Rings*, for just a week?

MARCH: Which singing siblings scored a Top 5 hit with the song *Sucker*?

APRIL: *When We All Fall Asleep, Where Do We Go?* debuted at Number 1 on the Official Albums chart for which artist?

MAY: The Top 3 hit *Me* was a collaboration on the Official Singles Chart between Taylor Swift and Brandon Urie, the lead singer of which American band?

JUNE: Name the Scotsman whose debut Number 1 on the Official Albums Chart was titled *Divinely Uninspired To A Hellish Extent*?

JULY: Camila Cabello joined Shawn Mendes on the Number 1 song *Señorita* – name the girl-group that Camila was part of in 2016 when they took the song *Work From Home* to Number 2?

AUGUST: How many *Nights* was Dominic Fike describing in the title of Official Singles Chart debut hit?

SEPTEMBER: DJ and producer Kygo took an old recording of Whitney Houston covering the song *Higher Love* and reached Number 2 with the new remix – in what year did the original version by Steve Winwood first appear inside the Top 40?

OCTOBER: Who did Jorja Smith team with for the Top 10 hit collaboration *Be Honest*.

NOVEMBER: *Good As Hell* became the first Top 10 hit on the Official Singles Chart for which US star?

DECEMBER: Rod Stewart's Christmas Number 1 on the Official Albums Chart contained new versions of his old songs, accompanied by The Royal Philharmonic Orchestra, and it had the same four-word title as a Number 3 hit of his that appeared on the Official Singles Chart back in 1977 – name it.

Answers on page 280

TOP 10: 31 OCTOBER 2019

Fill in the blanks from this complete Official Singles Chart Top 10. If the song title is listed, we're looking for the band or artist that's missing. If the band or artist is listed, we're looking for the missing song title.

1. (1) TONES & I ....

2. (2) .... *RIDE IT*

3. (4) .... *CIRCLES*

4. (7) ED SHEERAN, CAMILA CABELLO & CARDI B ....

5. (5) .... *HIGHEST IN THE ROOM*

6. (9) .... *BRUISES*

7. (6) X .... *OUTNUMBERED*

8. (11) AITCH FEATURING ZIEZIE ....

9. (8) JORJA SMITH FEATURING BURNA BOY ....

10. (19) .... *MEMORIES*

Answers on page 280

HEY LORD, DON'T ASK ME QUESTIONS

If you don't already know the amazing 1978 minor Top 40 hit by Graham Parker & The Rumour with that same title as our header, it's well worth checking out, but before you do, see if you can correctly identify the 20 acts who asked each of the following pop posers on the Official Singles Chart.

1.   *Why Does It Always Rain On Me?* [Number 10 in August 1999]

2.   *Is There Something I Should Know?* [Number 1 in March 1983]

3.   *What Have You Done For Me Lately?* [Number 2 in May 1986]

4.   *Are 'Friends' Electric?* [Number 1 in June 1979]

5.   *What's The Frequency, Kenneth?* [Number 9 in September 1994]

6.   *Have I The Right?* [Number 1 in August 1964]

7.   *Do You Really Like It?* [Number 1 in June 2001]

8.   *Knock Knock, Who's There?* [Number 2 in April 1970]

9.   *Why Don't You Get A Job?* [Number 2 in May 1999]

10. *What Do You Want?* [Number 1 in December 1959]

11. *Is It Any Wonder?* [Number 3 in June 2006]

12. *Ullo John, Gotta New Motor?* [Number 15 in March 1984]

13. *Donald, Where's Your Troosers?* [Number 4 in December 1989]

14. *Oh Babe, What Would You Say?* [Number 4 in June 1972]

15. *(How Much Is That) Doggie In The Window?* [Number 1 in April 1953]

16. *Why'd You Only Call Me When You're High?* [Number 8 in August 2013]

17. *What's New Pussycat?* [Number 11 in September 1965]

18. *Have You Ever Really Loved A Woman?* [Number 4 in April 1995]

19. *Who's Zoomin' Who?* [Number 11 in January 1986]

20. *What You Waiting For?* [Number 4 in November 2004]

Answers on page 280

THE WEEK AHEAD

The title speaks for itself – here are 20 songs that have all featured on the Official Singles Chart mentioning specific days of the week or referring to the week/weekend ahead of us.

Let's see how many artists you can correctly name.

1. *Friday I'm In Love* [Number 6 in June 1992]

2. *Sunday Girl* [Number 1 in May 1979]

3. *Saturday Night* [Number 1 in September 1994]

4. *I Don't Like Mondays* [Number 1 in July 1979]

5. *She Left Me On Friday* [Number 11 in March 1998]

6. *Ruby Tuesday* [Number 9 in November 1970]

7. *It's Good News Week* [Number 5 in November 1965]

8. *Every Day Is Like Sunday* [Number 9 in June 1988]

9. *Saturday Night's Alright For Fighting* [Number 7 in July 1973]

10. *Thursday* [Number 3 in December 2018]

11. *Freaky Friday* [Number 1 in April 2018]

12. *Wednesday Week* [Number 11 in August 1980]

13. *Funky Weekend* [Number 10 in March 1976]

14. *Friday's Child* [Number 4 in July 2004]

15. *Dancin' (On A Saturday Night)* [Number 2 in September 1973]

16. *Lazy Sunday* [Number 2 in May 1968]

17. *Seven Days And One Week* [Number 3 in October 1996]

18. *Pleasant Valley Sunday* [Number 11 in August 1967]

19. *Everything's Tuesday* [Number 12 in March 1971]

20. *One Week* [Number 5 in February 1999]

Answers on page 280-1

NUMBER 1 ALBUMS

Every one of these essential titles went all the way to Number 1 at some point since the first Official Albums Chart appeared back in 1956.

We've listed the month and the year that each of them topped the chart, rather than the date that they were originally released.

How many of the 40 bands or artists you can identify?

1.   *Tubular Bells* [October 1974]

2.   *Jagged Little Pill* [May 1996]

3.   *A Rush Of Blood To The Head* [September 2002]

4.   *Divinely Uninspired To A Hellish Extent* [May 2019]

5.   *Songs For Swingin' Lovers* [July 1956]

6.   *Goat's Head Soup* [September 1973]

7.   *Graceland* [October 1986]

8.   *Walthamstow* [February 1993]

9.   *Doo-Wops & Hooligans* [January 2011]

10. *Revolver* [August 1966]

11. *Kings Of The Wild Frontier* [January 1981]

12. *Tranquility Base Hotel & Casino* [May 2018]

13. *Arrival* [January 1977]

14. *The Man Who* [August 1999]

15. *Harvest* [March 1972]

16. *Popped In Souled Out* [January 1988]

17. *RENAISSANCE* [August 2022]

18. *Ten Good Reasons* [June 1989]

19. *A Question Of Balance* [August 1970]

20. *Sour* [June 2021]

21. *All Things Must Pass* [February 1971]

22. *The Final Cut* [April 1983]

23. *Life In Cartoon Motion* [February 2007]

24. *Bringing It All Back Home* [May 1965]

25. *25* [December 2015]

26. *Quench* [October 1998]

27. *Sunny Side Up* [June 2009]

28. *Stupidity* [October 1976]

29. *Future Nostalgia* [April 2020]

30. *Elephant* [April 2003]

31. *Every Picture Tells A Story* [October 1971]

32. *The Next Day* [March 2013]

33. *Ogden's Nut Gone Flake* [June 1968]

34. *Only By The Night* [October 2008]

35. *Replicas* [July 1979]

36. *Everybody Else Is Doing It, So Why Can't We?* [June 1994]

37. *Human's Lib* [March 1984]

38. *Kid A* [October 2000]

39. *Stanley Road* [May 1995]

40. *A Grand Don't Come For Free* [July 2004]

Answers on page 281

HIP-HOP LEGENDS

Every one of these 20 tracks is a genuine rap classic from one of the most acclaimed and influential acts of that genre.

All you need to do is name the hip-hop pioneers who brought these songs to the mainstream via the Official Singles Chart.

1.   *Lose Yourself* [Number 1 in December 2002]

2.   *99 Problems* [Number 12 in May 2004]

3.   *No Sleep Till Brooklyn* [Number 14 in June 1987]

4.   *Gravel Pit* [Number 6 in November 2000]

5.   *Don't Believe The Hype* [Number 18 in July 1988]

6.   *Can I Kick It?* [Number 15 in February 1991]

7.   *Tha Crossroads* [Number 8 in August 1996]

8.   *Rapper's Delight* [Number 3 in December 1979]

9.   *Eye Know* [Number 14 in November 1989]

10. *The Message* [Number 8 in September 1982]

11. *I Ain't Goin' Out Like That* [Number 15 in December 1993]

12. *The Lane* [Number 18 in December 1996]

13. *Ms Jackson* [Number 2 in March 2001]

14. *It's Tricky* [Number 16 in June 1987]

15. *Express Yourself* [Number 26 in June 1990]

16. *Paid In Full* [Number 15 in November 1987]

17. *Nuthin' But A 'G' Thang* [Number 31 in January 1994]

18. *I Ain't Mad At Cha* [Number 13 in November 1996]

19. *I Need Love* [Number 8 in October 1987]

20. *What's My Name?* [Number 20 in December 1993]

HIT AFTER HIT:
EMINEM

Place these five **EMINEM** hits in their correct chronological order as they each appeared on the Official Singles Chart.

A. JUST LOSE IT

B. WITHOUT ME

C. CLEANIN' OUT MY CLOSET

D. MY NAME IS

E. THE REAL SLIM SHADY

Answers on page 281

ONE TO FIVE:
SEAN PAUL

Each of these **SEAN PAUL** hits achieved a different peak position on the Official Singles Chart – put them in the correct order, starting with Number 1 and working your way down to Number 5.

A. GET BUSY

B. LIKE GLUE

C. GIMME THE LIGHT

D. WE BE BURNIN'

E. BREATHE (AS FEATURED ARTIST WITH BLU CANTRELL)

Answers on page 281

HIT AFTER HIT:
DRAKE

Place these five **DRAKE** hits in their correct chronological order as they each appeared on the Official Singles Chart.

A. HOTLINE BLING

B. MASSIVE

C. FAKE LOVE

D. GOD'S PLAN

E. NICE FOR WHAT

Answers on page 281

ONE TO FIVE:
CRAIG DAVID

Each of these **CRAIG DAVID** hits achieved a different peak position on the Official Singles Chart – put them in the correct order, starting with Number 1 and working your way down to Number 5.

A. RISE AND FALL (FEATURING STING)

B. WALKING AWAY

C. DON'T LOVE YOU NO MORE

D. I KNOW YOU (FEATURING BASTILLE)

E. 7 DAYS

Answers on page 281

LITTLE THINGS MEAN A LOT

It was the title of a Number 1 hit on the Official Singles Chart way back in 1954 for American singer Kitty Kallen, and it led us on the search for another 20 songs to challenge you with, all containing the word 'little'.

How many of the bands and artists can you name from this list of top tunes?

1. *Little Lies* [Number 5 in October 1987]

2. *A Little Less Conversation* [Number 1 in June 2002]

3. *Shine A Little Love* [Number 6 in June 1979]

4. *A Little Respect* [Number 4 in October 1988]

5. *Little Children* [Number 1 in March 1964]

6. *A Little Time* [Number 1 in October 1990]

7. *Little Things* [Number 1 in November 2012]

8. *Little Willy* [Number 4 in July 1972]

9. *Little Donkey* [Number 3 in December 1960]

10. *I've Got A Little Puppy* [Number 4 in September 1996]

11. *A Little Bit Of Luck* [Number 9 in January 2000]

12. *Three Little Pigs* [Number 5 in June 1993]

13. *Little White Bull* [Number 6 in January 1960]

14. *With A Little Luck* [Number 5 in April 1978]

15. *Little Arrows* [Number 2 in October 1968]

16. *Dance Little Lady Dance* [Number 6 in October 1976]

17. *Little Bit Of Love* [Number 7 in April 2021]

18. *A Little Bit Me, A Little Bit You* [Number 3 in April 1967]

19. *Too Little Too Late* [Number 4 in January 2007]

20. *Little Red Rooster* [Number 1 in December 1964]

Answers on page 281-2

SUPERSTAR SPOTLIGHT:
BEYONCÉ

1. Destiny's Child made their Official Singles Chart debut with the song *No, No, No* going straight in the Top 5, but in what year?

2. Which 2000 film featured the Destiny's Child Number 1 song *Independent Women Part 1* on the soundtrack?

3. In 2001, Destiny's Child covered the song *Emotion*, and it gave the group a ninth Top 10 entry – who had the original Official Singles Chart hit with it in 1978?

4. How many weeks did *Crazy In Love* spend at Number 1 on the Official Singles Chart in 2003?

5. Beyoncé collaborated with which other singer on the 2007 Number 1 song *Beautiful Liar*?

6. Place these five Beyoncé hits in their correct chronological order as they each appeared on the Official Singles Chart.

    a. *Best Thing I Never Had*
    b. *Sweet Dreams*
    c. *If I Were A Boy*
    d. *Halo*
    e. *Baby Boy featuring Sean Paul*

Answers on page 282

HIT AFTER HIT:
TAYLOR SWIFT

Each of these **TAYLOR SWIFT** hits achieved a different peak position on the Official Singles Chart – put them in the correct order, starting with Number 1 and working your way down to Number 5.

A. LOOK WHAT YOU MADE ME DO

B. WILLOW

C. YOU NEED TO CALM DOWN

D. SHAKE IT OFF

E. WE ARE NEVER EVER GETTING BACK TOGETHER

Answers on page 282

ONE TO FIVE:
MARIAH CAREY

Each of these **MARIAH CAREY** hits achieved a different peak position on the Official Singles Chart – put them in the correct order, starting with Number 1 and working your way down to Number 5.

A. FANTASY

B. I'LL BE THERE

C. TOUCH MY BODY

D. HONEY

E. WITHOUT YOU

Answers on page 282

SOMETHING IN THE AIR

You should already know that our title for this section comes from Thunderclap Newman's great July 1969 Number 1 song, and it was the inspiration for these 20 other hits from seven decades of the Official Singles Chart, all of which you'll find high in the sky, so who performed them?

1.   *When Doves Cry* [Number 4 in July 1984]

2.   *Albatross* [Number 1 in January 1969]

3.   *I'm Like A Bird* [Number 5 in March 2001]

4.   *Songbird* [Number 3 in February 2003]

5.   *Wind Beneath My Wings* [Number 3 in November 1997]

6.   *Little Bird* [Number 3 in February 1993]

7.   *The Birdie Song (Birdie Dance)* [Number 2 in October 1981]

8.   *Dove (I'll Be Loving You)* [Number 9 in June 2002]

9.   *Pretty Flamingo* [Number 1 in May 1966]

10. *Wings Of A Dove* [Number 2 in September 1983]

11. *Sing Little Birdie* [Number 12 in April 1959]

12. *Bird Of Paradise* [Number 6 in January 1984]

13. *Mockingbird* [Number 4 in May 2005]

14. *The Sparrow Song* [Number 11 in November 1979]

15. *Flying* [Number 4 in October 1996]

16. *Et Les Oiseaux Chantaient (And The Birds Were Singing)* [Number 4 in October 1980]

17. *Stool Pigeon* [Number 7 in August 1982]

18. *Fly Like An Eagle* [Number 13 in March 1997]

19. *Wings* [Number 1 in September 2012]

20. *Ride A White Swan* [Number 2 in January 1971]

Answers on page 282

HIT AFTER HIT:
DUA LIPA

Place these five **DUA LIPA** hits in their correct chronological order as they each appeared on the Official Singles Chart.

A. NEW RULES

B. LEVITATING

C. BE THE ONE

D. DON'T START NOW

E. PHYSICAL

Answers on page 282

ONE TO FIVE:
USHER

Each of these **USHER** hits achieved a different peak position on the Official Singles Chart – put them in the correct order, starting with Number 1 and working your way down to Number 5.

A. BURN

B. LOVE IN THIS CLUB (FEATURING YOUNG JEEZY)

C. U GOT IT BAD

D. U REMIND ME

E. POP YA COLLAR

Answers on page 282

WE ARE FAMILY

Mums, dads, sisters, brothers, cousins, grandparents, and other assorted relatives are always rich pickings when it comes to song titles.

We've pulled together 40 memorable family-themed hits from every decade that the Official Singles Chart has been in existence.

How many of the artists can you name?

1. *Running In The Family* [Number 6 in March 1987]

2. *Does Your Mother Know?* [Number 4 in May 1979]

3. *There's No One Quite Like Grandma* [Number 1 in December 1980]

4. *Father Figure* [Number 11 in January 1988]

5. *Annie I'm Not Your Daddy* [Number 2 in October 1982]

6. *Father And Son* [Number 2 in December 1995]

7. *Hey Brother* [Number 2 in December 2013]

8. *Mama Weer All Crazee Now* [Number 1 in September 1972]

9. *The Family Madrigal* [Number 7 in February 2022]

10. *Daddy Cool* [Number 6 on February 1977]

11. *Mama Do The Hump* [Number 2 in January 2012]

12. *Grandad* [Number 1 in January 1971]

13. *Dance With My Father* [Number 21 in February 2004]

14. *Uncle Sam* [Number 21 in November 1985]

15. *Mama Do (Uh Oh, Oh Oh)* [Number 1 in June 2009]

16. *3 Is Family* [Number 9 in July 1995]

17. *Cousin Norman* [Number 6 in October 1971]

18. *Mother And Child Reunion* [Number 5 in March 1972]

19. *In The Name Of The Father* [Number 8 in August 1995]

20. *Mama* [Number 4 in September 1983]

21. *Dance Little Sister* [Number 20 in October 1987]

22. *Family Portrait* [Number 11 in December 2002]

23. *Grandma's Party* [Number 9 in January 1977]

24. *Family Man* [Number 15 in May 1983]

25. *Hey, Soul Sister* [Number 18 in May 2010]

26. *Oh Mein Papa* [Number 1 in January 1954]

27. *Listen To Your Father* [Number 23 in November 1984]

28. *Have You Seen Your Mother, Baby, Standing In The Shadow?* [Number 5 in October 1966]

29. *Like Sister And Brother* [Number 7 in September 1973]

30. *Daddy's Home* [Number 2 in December 1981]

31. *Mother Of Mine* [Number 2 in January 1972]

32. *Hey Mama* [Number 6 in March 2004]

33. *Sister Of Mercy* [Number 11 in July 1984]

34. *Son Of My Father* [Number 1 in February 1972]

35. *Sylvia's Mother* [Number 2 in July 1972]

36. *Mother Nature And Father Time* [Number 7 in October 1953]

37. *Brother Louie* [Number 4 in August 1986]

38. *Mother's Talk* [Number 14 in September 1984]

39. *My Brother Jake* [Number 4 in June 1971]

40. *Family Affair* [Number 15 in February 1972]

Answers on page 282-3

SUPERSTAR SPOTLIGHT:
ED SHEERAN

1. In what year did Ed make both his Official Singles Chart and Official Albums Chart debut?

2. Ed wrote and sang guest vocals on which 2015 Number 1 song for Justin Bieber?

3. When Ed released his 2017 album *Divide*, he placed nine of the songs from it inside the Top 10 on the Official Singles Chart during its opening week – which two acts collaborated on the only non-Ed hit inside the Top 10 at that time?

4. How many years' gap was there between Ed achieving his first Number 1 song with *Sing* and his tenth with *Bad Habits*?

5. *Strip That Down* was a Top 3 hit in 2017 that Ed wrote for which former member of One Direction?

6. Each of these Ed hits achieved a different peak position on the Official Singles Chart – put them in the correct order, starting with Number 1 and working your way down to Number 5.

   a. *Galway Girl*
   b. *Thinking Out Loud*
   c. *Lego House*
   d. *Overpass Graffiti*
   e. *The A Team*

Answers on page 283

HIT AFTER HIT:
NEW KIDS ON THE BLOCK

Place these nineties hits by **NEW KIDS ON THE BLOCK** in their correct chronological order as they appeared on the Official Singles Chart during that decade.

A. THIS ONE'S FOR THE CHILDREN

B. TONIGHT

C. STEP BY STEP

D. COVER GIRL

E. HANGIN' TOUGH

Answers on page 283

ONE TO FIVE:
JUSTIN BIEBER

Each of these **JUSTIN BIEBER** hits achieved a different peak position on the Official Singles Chart – put them in the correct order, starting with Number 1 and working your way down to Number 5.

A. BABY (FEATURING LUDACRIS)

B. BOYFRIEND

C. YUMMY

D. WHAT DO YOU MEAN?

E. ANYONE

Answers on page 283

SPOTLIGHT:
2020s

MONTH BY MONTH: 2020

All data below refers to positions achieved on the Official Singles Chart or (where relevant) the Official Albums Chart.

JANUARY: Who did Eminem collaborate with on his Number 1 song *Godzilla*?

FEBRUARY: Name Roddy Ricch's first Top 10 hit on the Official Singles Chart, which peaked at Number 2.

MARCH: What was the one-word title of the Number 1 hit by SAINt JHN?

APRIL: A charity reworking of *You'll Never Walk Alone* by Captain Tom Moore, Michael Ball & The NHS Voices Of Care Choir debuted at Number 1 – in what year did Gerry & The Pacemakers first take their version of the song to Number 1?

MAY: During the pandemic, BBC Radio 1 pulled together famous musicians from around the world under the name of the Live Lounge Allstars – which Foo Fighters hit did they cover and take to Number 1 on the Official Singles Chart?

JUNE: Name the two female stars who teamed up for the Number 1 hit *Rain On Me*.

JULY: *Rough And Rowdy Ways* went to Number 1 on the Official Albums Chart for which iconic musician?

AUGUST: *Head And Heart* by Joel Corry featuring MNEK had the longest unbroken run at Number 1 for any song on the Official Singles Chart during 2020 – for how many weeks did it remain on top?

SEPTEMBER: Tate McRae made her Top 40 debut with which song?

OCTOBER: Which musician was at Number 2 on the Official Singles Chart with his AJ Tracey and Stormzy collaboration *Ain't It Different* in the same week that he landed the new Number 1 on the Official Albums Chart with *Edna*.

NOVEMBER: An all-star charity cover of which 2002 Oasis hit raised funds for BBC Children In Need when it entered the Top 10 on the Official Singles Chart?

DECEMBER: *All I Want For Christmas* by Mariah Carey finally made its way to Number 1, but in what year did the song get stuck at Number 2 on the festive countdown behind East 17's *Stay Another Day*?

Answers on page 283

TOP 10: 21 MAY 2020

Fill in the blanks from this complete Official Singles
Chart Top 10. If the song title is listed, we're looking for
the band or artist that's missing. If the band or artist
is listed, we're looking for the missing song title.

1. (6) DABABY FEATURING RODDY RICCH ....

2. (1) .... *TOOSIE SLIDE*

3. (2) .... *SAY SO*

4. (NEW) ARIANA GRANDE & JUSTIN BIEBER ....

5. (4) POWFU FEATURING BEABADOOBEE ....

6. (NEW) .... *GOOBA*

7. (5) .... *BLINDING LIGHTS*

8. (7) S1MBA FEATURING DTG ....

9. (3) .... *SAVAGE*

10. (8) .... *DINNER GUEST*

Answers on page 283

MONTH BY MONTH: 2021

All data below refers to positions achieved on the Official Singles Chart or (where relevant) the Official Albums Chart.

JANUARY: The debut single for American rapper CJ became a Top 3 hit on the Official Singles Chart – what was the song title?

FEBRUARY: Taylor Swift's brand-new re-recorded version of her 2009 debut hit song appeared inside the Top 20 – can you name the track?

MARCH: London-based rap duo A1 x J1 landed a Number 2 hit with which song?

APRIL: Who began the month at Number 1 on the Official Singles Chart with his reworking of the traditional sea shanty *Wellerman*?

MAY: Which rock duo returned after a four-year break and scored their third consecutive Number 1 on the Official Albums Chart with *Typhoons*?

JUNE: The song *Zitti E Buoni* by Måneskin entered the Top 20 on the Official Singles Chart after winning the Eurovision Song Contest – what nationality are the band?

JULY: A Number 2 hit for KSI shared the same title with a totally different song that gave Madonna her Top 40 debut in 1984 – name it.

AUGUST: Which American rock band went straight in at Number 1 on the Official Albums Chart with *Pressure Machine*?

SEPTEMBER: ABBA scored two simultaneous Top 20 hits on the Official Singles Chart – one song was *I Still Have Faith In You*, but what was the other?

OCTOBER: Which K-pop group teamed up with Coldplay for the Top 3 hit *My Universe*?

NOVEMBER: For three consecutive weeks this month, Ed Sheeran had three simultaneous Top 5 hits with *Shivers*, *Bad Habits*, and which other song?

DECEMBER: *Rockin' Around The Christmas Tree* by Brenda Lee made yet another festive appearance on the Official Singles Chart, but in what year did it make its original Top 10 debut?

TOP 10: 27 MAY 2021

Fill in the blanks from this complete Official Singles Chart Top 10. If the song title is listed, we're looking for the band or artist that's missing. If the band or artist is listed, we're looking for the missing song title.

1. (1) TION WAYNE & RUSS MILLIONS ....

2. (NEW) .... GOOD 4 U

3. (3) DOJA CAT FEATURING SZA ....

4. (2) .... MONTERO (CALL ME BY YOUR NAME)

5. (5) .... SAVE YOUR TEARS

6. (4) JOEL CORRY, RAYE & DAVID GUETTA ....

7. (6) JUSTIN BIEBER FEATURING DANIEL CAESAR & GIVEON ....

8. (7) RITON & NIGHTCRAWLERS FEATURING HYPEMAN & MUFASA ....

9. (9) RAG'N'BONE MAN & P!NK ....

10. (8) .... LITTLE BIT OF LOVE

Answers on page 283

HIT AFTER HIT:
THE KILLERS

Place these five hits by **THE KILLERS** in their correct chronological order as they each appeared on the Official Singles Chart.

A. HUMAN

B. READ MY MIND

C. WHEN YOU WERE YOUNG

D. MR. BRIGHTSIDE

E. SMILE LIKE YOU MEAN IT

Answers on page 283

ONE TO FIVE:
LEONA LEWIS

Each of these **LEONA LEWIS** hits achieved a different peak position on the Official Singles Chart – put them in the correct order, starting with Number 1 and working your way down to Number 5.

A. COLLIDE (WITH AVICII)

B. HAPPY

C. FORGIVE ME

D. RUN

E. ONE MORE SLEEP

Answers on page 283

SUPERSTAR SPOTLIGHT:
ADELE

1. What total number do you get if you add together the titles of Adele's first four albums?

2. In the first 70 years of the Official Singles Chart, how many Number 1 songs has she had?

3. Complete the four missing words from this 2016 Top 5 hit: *Send My Love (___ ___ ___ ___)*

4. In what year did Adele reach Number 2 on the Official Singles Chart with her theme song to the James Bond film *Skyfall*?

5. Adele's cover of *Make You Feel My Love* featured on her debut album, and it later became a Top 5 hit for her, but which legendary musician wrote the song?

6. Place these five Adele hits in their correct chronological order as they each appeared on the Official Singles Chart.

   a. *Easy On Me*
   b. *When We Were Young*
   c. *Oh My God*
   d. *Hometown Glory*
   e. *Set Fire To The Rain*

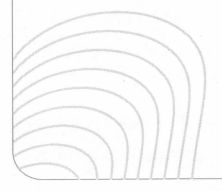

Answers on page 283-4

HIT AFTER HIT:
THE HUMAN LEAGUE

Place these five **HUMAN LEAGUE** hits in their correct chronological order as they each appeared on the Official Singles Chart.

A. TELL ME WHEN

B. MIRROR MAN

C. HUMAN

D. THE SOUND OF THE CROWD

E. LIFE ON YOUR OWN

Answers on page 284

ONE TO FIVE:
THE BEACH BOYS

Each of these **BEACH BOYS** hits achieved a different peak position on the Official Singles Chart – put them in the correct order, starting with Number 1 and working your way down to Number 5.

A. BARBARA ANN

B. GOD ONLY KNOWS

C. COTTONFIELDS

D. GOOD VIBRATIONS

E. THEN I KISSED HER

Answers on page 284

HIT AFTER HIT:
KOOL & THE GANG

Place these eighties hits by **KOOL & THE GANG** in their correct chronological order as they appeared on the Official Singles Chart during that decade.

A. CELEBRATION

B. GET DOWN ON IT

C. FRESH

D. CHERISH

E. (WHEN YOU SAY YOU LOVE SOMEBODY) IN THE HEART

Answers on page 284

ONE TO FIVE:
WHITNEY HOUSTON

Each of these **WHITNEY HOUSTON** hits achieved a different peak position on the Official Singles Chart – put them in the correct order, starting with Number 1 and working your way down to Number 5.

A. I HAVE NOTHING

B. MY LOVE IS YOUR LOVE

C. ONE MOMENT IN TIME

D. I'M YOUR BABY TONIGHT

E. I'M EVERY WOMAN

Answers on page 284

HIT AFTER HIT:
SHAKIN' STEVENS

Place these eighties hits by **SHAKIN' STEVENS** in their correct chronological order as they appeared on the Official Singles Chart during that decade.

A. A LOVE WORTH WAITING FOR

B. CRY JUST A LITTLE BIT

C. GREEN DOOR

D. THIS OLE HOUSE

E. YOU DRIVE ME CRAZY

Answers on page 284

ONE TO FIVE:
BRITNEY SPEARS

Each of these **BRITNEY SPEARS** hits achieved a different peak position on the Official Singles Chart – put them in the correct order, starting with Number 1 and working your way down to Number 5.

A. I'M NOT A GIRL, NOT YET A WOMAN

B. TOXIC

C. I'M A SLAVE 4 U

D. SOMETIMES

E. LUCKY

Answers on page 284

CHRISTMAS NUMBER 1s?

Only a very select bunch of the festive favourites listed here were, in fact, crowned Christmas Number 1 on the Official Singles Chart, but can you spot which ones?

Don't get caught out – a few of these hits may have reached Number 1 at some point in their chart history, but they weren't at the top of the chart on Christmas Day itself!

1. Bing Crosby – *White Christmas*

2. Bon Jovi – *Please Come Home For Christmas*

3. Coldplay – *Christmas Lights*

4. Dickie Valentine – *Christmas Alphabet*

5. The Darkness – *Christmas Time (Don't Let The Bells End)*

6. Elton John – *Step Into Christmas*

7. Geraldine – *Once Upon A Christmas Song*

8. Greg Lake – *I Believe In Father Christmas*

9. Jane McDonald – *Cruise Into Christmas*

10. Jess Glynne – *This Christmas*

11. John & Yoko And The Plastic Ono Band With The Harlem Community Choir – *Happy Xmas (War Is Over)*

12. Mariah Carey – *All I Want For Christmas Is You*

13. Mud – *Lonely This Christmas*

14. Paul McCartney – *Wonderful Christmastime*

15. Queen – *Thank God It's Christmas*

16. Shakin' Stevens – *Merry Christmas Everyone*

17. Slade – *Merry Xmas Everybody*

18. Wham! – *Last Christmas*

19. Wizzard – *I Wish It Could Be Christmas Everyday*

20. The Wombles – *Wombling Merry Christmas*

Answers on page 284

WHEN YOU'RE GONE

There's only one way to finish things off, and that's with a bunch of songs all loosely based around goodbyes.

See how many correct artist names you can match to these 20 hit titles from the Official Singles Chart during its first 70 years.

1.   *Hello, Goodbye* [Number 1 in December 1967]

2.   *Here's Where The Story Ends* [Number 7 in March 1998]

3.   *Never Can Say Goodbye* [Number 2 in January 1975]

4.   *See You Later, Alligator* [Number 7 in March 1956]

5.   *Say Hello Wave Goodbye* [Number 3 in February 1982]

6.   *Farewell Is A Lonely Sound* [Number 8 in May 1970]

7.   *Goodbye My Love* [Number 4 in April 1965]

8.   *To The End* [Number 16 in June 1994]

9.   *Never Goodbye* [Number 9 in April 1962]

10. *Disappear* [Number 21 in December 1990]

11. *Kiss And Say Goodbye* [Number 4 in July 1976]

12. *The Minute You're Gone* [Number 1 in April 1965]

13. *Ev'ry Time We Say Goodbye* [Number 11 in December 1987]

14. *Gone Gone Gone* [Number 15 in September 1979]

15. *End Of The Line* [Number 5 in December 1998]

16. *The Last Farewell* [Number 2 in September 1975]

17. *No More* [Number 6 in March 2001]

18. *Goodbye-ee* [Number 18 in July 1965]

19. *The Bitter End* [Number 12 in March 2003]

20. *Goodbye* [Number 1 in December 1998]

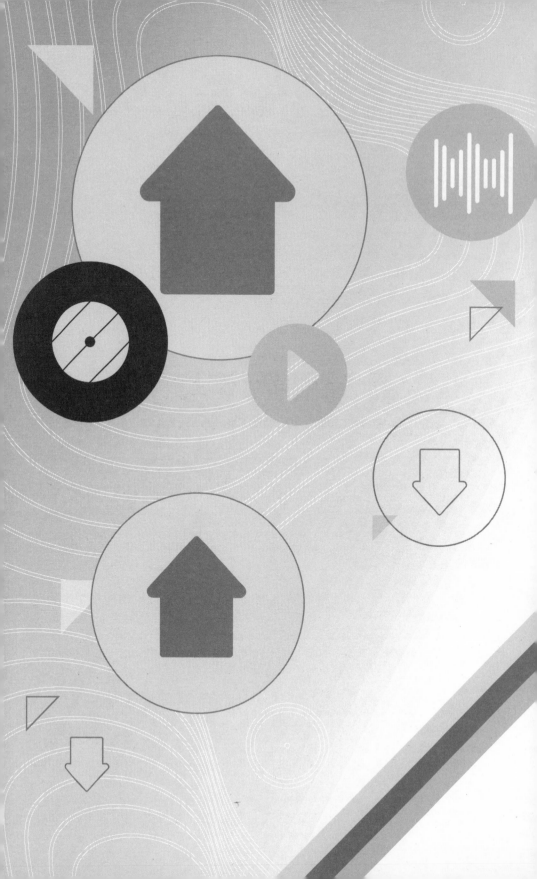

ANSWERS

STARTING TOGETHER

1. Red
2. Men
3. Stone
4. Black
5. Cat
6. Harry
7. Paul
8. Girls
9. Holly
10. Taylor
11. System
12. Faith
13. Joel
14. Sister
15. Machine
16. Joy
17. Charles
18. Dennis
19. Arthur
20. House
21. Lee
22. Status
23. Scott
24. Leon
25. Michael
26. Wayne
27. Martin
28. Dean
29. Echo
30. Beach
31. Noel
32. Club
33. Hollywood
34. Paris
35. Thomas
36. Eve
37. Pop
38. Marie
39. Simon
40. Wilson

COME TOGETHER

1. Bob Marley
2. Smokey Robinson
3. Yazz
4. Sly
5. Gladys Knight
6. Katrina
7. Frankie Lymon
8. Derek
9. Ian Dury
10. Doctor
11. Reverend
12. Harold Melvin
13. Marina
14. Flash
15. B. Bumble
16. Brian Poole
17. KC
18. Kid Creole
19. Father Abraham
20. Lloyd Cole
21. Huey Lewis
22. Reparata
23. Joe Brown
24. Johnny Kidd
25. Martha Reeves
26. Laurie Lingo
27. Jonathan Richman
28. Cliff Bennett
29. Disco Tex
30. Doug E. Fresh
31. Archie Bell
32. Mike
33. Freddie
34. Bruce Hornsby
35. Heavy D
36. Joan Jett
37. Gerry
38. Tommy James
39. Rocky Sharpe
40. Jive Bunny

MILLION SELLERS

1. Gloria Gaynor
2. Ray Parker Jr
3. One Direction
4. Aerosmith
5. Dawn featuring Tony Orlando

6. Black Box
7. Ed Sheeran
8. Gotye featuring Kimbra
9. The Seekers
10. Art Garfunkel
11. Natalie Imbruglia
12. Brotherhood Of Man
13. Eiffel 65
14. Shayne Ward
15. The New Seekers
16. Tight Fit
17. Swedish House Mafia featuring John Martin
18. Cheryl Cole
19. Mr Acker Bilk with The Leon Young String Chorale
20. Celine Dion

HIT AFTER HIT / ONE TO FIVE

The Rolling Stones: a-b-e-c-d
The Kinks: e-b-c-a-d

HIT AFTER HIT / ONE TO FIVE

Diana Ross: c-b-e-d-a
Cliff Richard: b-a-c-e-d

THE FIFTIES (PART ONE)

1. Bill Haley & His Comets
2. Paul Anka
3. Harry Belafonte
4. Emile Ford & The Checkmates
5. Elvis Presley
6. Adam Faith
7. Cliff Richard And The Shadows
8. Elvis Presley
9. Pat Boone
10. Buddy Holly

THE FIFTIES (PART TWO)

1. Perry Como
2. Doris Day
3. Tennessee Ernie Ford

4. Slim Whitman
5. Connie Francis
6. Guy Mitchell
7. Lord Rockingham's XI
8. Ruby Murray
9. Frankie Laine
10. Johnnie Ray

SUPERSTAR SPOTLIGHT: ELVIS PRESLEY

1. Heartbreak Hotel
2. All Shook Up
3. Are You Lonesome Tonight
4. 21
5. 1987
6. e-a-d-b-c

NUMBER 1 MILESTONES

1: Here In My Heart
100: Do You Mind?
200: Help!
250: Young Girl
300: Knock Three Times
400: Don't Cry For Me Argentina
500: A Little Peace
600: China In Your Hand
700: Twist And Shout
750: What Becomes Of The Broken Hearted / Saturday Night At The Movies / You'll Never Walk Alone
800: Bootie Call
900: Lady Marmalade
1000: One Night / I Got Stung
1100: Evacuate The Dancefloor
1200: This Is Love
1250: Rather Be
1300: Fight Song
1400: B.O.T.A. (Baddest Of Them All)

HIT AFTER HIT / ONE TO FIVE

Cher: a-e-b-d-c
Stevie Wonder: b-c-a-d-e

BACK TO THE SIXTIES

1. The Beach Boys
2. The Rolling Stones
3. Procol Harum
4. Ike & Tina Turner
5. Billy Fury
6. The Byrds
7. The Everly Brothers
8. The Tornados
9. Sonny & Cher
10. Zager And Evans
11. The Kingsmen
12. Dusty Springfield
13. The Kinks
14. Sandie Shaw
15. The Marmalade
16. Ray Charles
17. Otis Redding
18. Helen Shapiro
19. The Small Faces
20. Glen Campbell
21. Pink Floyd
22. Johnny Cash
23. Jim Reeves
24. The Drifters
25. Marvin Gaye
26. Bob Dylan
27. Del Shannon
28. The Four Tops
29. The Moody Blues
30. The Archies
31. Engelbert Humperdinck
32. Frank Ifield
33. Cream
34. Mama Cass
35. The Righteous Brothers
36. The Animals
37. The Troggs
38. The Foundations
39. Sam Cooke
40. Chubby Checker
41. Bobby Darin
42. The McCoys
43. Aretha Franklin
44. The Temptations
45. The Shangri-Las
46. Richard Harris
47. Lonnie Donegan
48. Peter Sarstedt
49. Chris Farlowe
50. The Dave Clark Five
51. The Yardbirds
52. Creedence Clearwater Revival
53. The Ronettes
54. The Monkees
55. The Zombies
56. Steppenwolf
57. The Crystals
58. Stevie Wonder
59. The Who
60. The Beatles

SUPERSTAR SPOTLIGHT: THE BEATLES

1. 17 singles and 10 albums
2. *She Loves You*
3. 1982
4. *Free As A Bird*
5. George Harrison with *My Sweet Lord* in 1971
6. f-c-d-j-a-g-h-e-i-b

HIT AFTER HIT / ONE TO FIVE

Donna Summer: b-a-c-e-d
Bee Gees: a-e-c-b-d

THE FIRST TIME

1. The Police
2. Outkast
3. Little Mix
4. Dire Straits
5. The Corrs
6. Shakin' Stevens
7. Maroon 5
8. The Smiths
9. Coldplay
10. Eternal
11. Depeche Mode

12. Amy Winehouse
13. Oasis
14. P!nk
15. All Saints
16. Daryl Hall and John Oates
17. Snow Patrol
18. Jason Donovan
19. Paolo Nutini
20. Toni Braxton

CLOSE BUT NO CIGAR

1. Hot Chocolate
2. T. Rex
3. Roxy Music
4. Elvis Presley
5. Candi Staton
6. Elvis Costello And
   The Attractions
7. Petula Clark
8. Boney M
9. Squeeze
10. Billy Ocean
11. The Carpenters
12. Millie
13. Free
14. The Move
15. David Bowie
16. The Everly Brothers
17. Bachman-Turner Overdrive
18. Little Eva
19. Sparks
20. The Osmonds

HIT AFTER HIT / ONE TO FIVE

Olivia Newton-John: b-e-a-d-c
Elton John: d-a-b-e-c

70 FROM THE SEVENTIES

1. Glen Campbell
2. George Harrison
3. The Goodies
4. *Virginia Plain*
5. Joe Jackson
6. 1972

7. Eight
8. *Machine Gun*
9. Darts
10. *You To Me Are Everything*
11. Barbados
12. Emerson Lake & Palmer
13. Paper Lace
14. *The Man Who Sold The World*
15. *Voulez-Vous*
16. *Boogie Nights*
17. The Sweet
18. *From New York To LA*
19. *The Show Must Go On*
20. Billy Ocean
21. *Tapestry*
22. Supertramp
23. Bay City Rollers
24. Barry White
25. Meri Wilson
26. *Angel Fingers*
27. Lene Lovich
28. Carly Simon
29. Venus
30. *Rubber Bullets*
31. Squeeze
32. *And I Love You So*
33. *Cos I Luv You*
34. Marvin Gaye
35. Lindisfarne
36. Tammy Wynette
37. Nick Lowe
38. *You Just Might See Me Cry*
39. Jimmy Helms
40. X-Ray Spex
41. *Jolene*
42. Pink Floyd
43. Lena Martell
44. Robin Sarstedt
45. Peters & Lee
46. *Love To Love You Baby*
47. Sheena
48. 1975
49. Hank Mizell
50. *Chirpy Chirpy Cheep Cheep*
51. The Motors
52. Rubettes

53. The Rolling Stones
54. Luxembourg
55. Olivia Newton-John
56. KC & The Sunshine Band
57. Three
58. Andy Kim
59. *Into The Valley*
60. Neil Sedaka
61. C.W McCall
62. Judas Priest
63. Baccara
64. Benny Hill
65. *Walking On The Moon*
66. The Isley Brothers
67. *Voodoo Chile*
68. James Galway
69. *So You Win Again*
70. 1971

SUPERSTAR SPOTLIGHT: DAVID BOWIE

1. 6 years and two months (September 1979 to November 1975)
2. *All The Young Dudes*
3. Queen (*Under Pressure*) and Mick Jagger (*Dancing In The Street*)
4. *Aladdin Sane* and *Pinups*
5. *Blackstar*
6. c-a-e-b-d

LONDON SONGS

1. The Clash
2. Gerry Rafferty
3. Pet Shop Boys
4. Ed Sheeran featuring Stomzy
5. The Fratellis
6. AJ Tracey
7. London Boys
8. Dave
9. The New Vaudeville Band
10. Carter The Unstoppable Sex Machine

11. Electric Light Orchestra
12. Elvis Costello
13. Suggs
14. Fergie
15. Tottenham Hotspur FA Cup Final Squad featuring Chas & Dave
16. Eddy Grant
17. Ralph McTell
18. Cathy Dennis
19. Lily Allen
20. The Jam

HIT AFTER HIT / ONE TO FIVE

Boney M: c-a-e-d-b
Showaddywaddy: d-e-a-b-c

TRUE COLORS

1. Blue
2. Pink
3. Black
4. White
5. Brown
6. Pink
7. Brown
8. Black
9. Orange
10. Yellow
11. White
12. Black
13. Red
14. Blue
15. Pink
16. White
17. Blue
18. Green
19. Black
20. Blue

HIT AFTER HIT / ONE TO FIVE

Slade: e-d-a-b-c
Rod Stewart: b-d-a-e-c

MONTH BY MONTH: 1980

Jan: The Nolans
Feb: The Ramones
Mar: *Echo Beach*
Apr: *Poison Ivy*
May: The Human League
Jun: Stacy Lattisaw
Jul: *To Be Or Not To Be*
Aug: *Private Life*
Sep: Mungo Jerry – their Number 1 hit was *In The Summertime*
Oct: Barbra Streisand
Nov: *Minder*
Dec: Stray Cats

TOP 10: 1980

1. The Jam
2. *Together We Are Beautiful*
3. *Take That Look Off Your Face*
4. *Turning Japanese*
5. Liquid Gold
6. Peter Gabriel
7. Blondie
8. The Detroit Spinners
9. Rainbow
10. *Do That To Me One More Time*

MONTH BY MONTH: 1981

Jan: Chas & Dave
Feb: *The Oldest Swinger In Town*
Mar: *Jealous Guy*
Apr: Sid Owen
May: Tenpole Tudor
Jun: Toyah
Jul: Bad Manners
Aug: Aneka
Sept: *Pretend*
Oct: Barbara Gaskin
Nov: Elvis Costello
Dec: Godley & Crème

TOP 10: 1981

1. *Being With You*
2. Michael Jackson
3. *More Than In Love*
4. Red Sovine
5. *How 'Bout Us*
6. Odyssey
7. Adam & The Ants
8. Hazel O'Connor
9. Ultravox
10. Shakin' Stevens

MONTH BY MONTH: 1982

Jan: *Being Boiled*
Feb: Kraftwerk
Mar: Bow Wow Wow
Apr: Derek & The Dominoes
May: *I Should Have Known Better*
Jun: Richard Blackwood
Jul: *Las Palabras De Amor*
Aug: Kid Creole & The Coconuts
Sep: Donnie Calvin
Oct: *Mad World*
Nov: *Theme From Harry's Game*
Dec: Bing Crosby

TOP 10: 1982

1. *Come On Eileen*
2. *Eye Of The Tiger*
3. Soft Cell
4. Boystown Gang
5. Duran Duran
6. Irene Cara
7. *Hi-Fidelity*
8. Yazoo
9. *I Eat Cannibals*
10. Haircut 100

MONTH BY MONTH: 1983

Jan: Luude
Feb: Steam
Mar: Icehouse
Apr: Kenny Everett

May: Booker Newberry III
Jun: *Just Got Lucky*
Jul: *Baby Jane*
Aug: *The Crown*
Sep: Ryan Paris
Oct: *The Safety Dance*
Nov: Feargal Sharkey
Dec: Barry Manilow

TOP 10: 1983

1. Culture Club
2. Tracey Ullman
3. *Dear Prudence*
4. David Bowie
5. Howard Jones
6. *This Is Not A Love Song*
7. George Benson
8. UB40
9. *Blue Monday*
10. David Essex

MONTH BY MONTH: 1984

Jan: *Nobody Told Me*
Feb: Rockwell
Mar: Sade
Apr: Scritti Politti
May: Womack & Womack
Jun: Ultravox
Jul: Ollie & Jerry
Aug: Trevor Walters
Sep: Alphaville
Oct: Giorgio Moroder
Nov: Kajagoogoo
Dec: Five

TOP 10: 1984

1. *Relax*
2. Queen
3. The Thompson Twins
4. Cyndi Lauper
5. *Break My Stride*
6. Madonna
7. *That's Livin' Alright*
8. The Style Council

9. Duran Duran
10. *Love Theme From 'The Thorn Birds'*

MONTH BY MONTH: 1985

Jan: *Everything She Wants*
Feb: *A New England*
Mar: The Detroit Spinners
Apr: Lionel Richie
May: Steve Arrington
Jun: Fine Young Cannibals
Jul: *Ben*
Aug: Princess
Sep: Colonel Abrams
Oct: Slik
Nov: The Far Corporation
Dec: *Road To Nowhere*

TOP 10: 1985

1. *You Spin Me Round (Like A Record)*
2. *Easy Lover*
3. Madonna
4. *Kiss Me*
5. The Commodores
6. David Cassidy
7. Jermaine Jackson
8. *I Know Him So Well*
9. Paul Young
10. Prince & The Revolution

MONTH BY MONTH: 1986

Jan: Cherrelle
Feb: Swiss
Mar: 'Christopher'
Apr: *You To Me Are Everything*
May: 1969
Jun: *I Can Wait*
Jul: Max Headroom
Aug: *Let's Go All The Way*
Sep: Chicago
Oct: Nick Berry
Nov: Spandau Ballet
Dec: *Caravan Of Love*

TOP 10: 1986

1. *I Want To Wake Up With You*
2. *The Lady In Red*
3. Sinitta
4. *Anyone Can Fall In Love*
5. *Ain't Nothin' Goin' On But The Rent*
6. *Calling All The Heroes*
7. Lionel Richie
8. Phil Fearon
9. *Camouflage*
10. Lulu

MONTH BY MONTH: 1987

Jan: Robbie Nevil
Feb: The Blow Monkeys
Mar: *If You Let Me Stay*
Apr: The Pogues & The Dubliners
May: Johnny Hates Jazz
Jun: *Star Trekkin'*
Jul: Hue & Cry
Aug: Boogie Box High
Sep: Black
Oct: Steve Walsh
Nov: *Bridge Of Spies*
Dec: Ketty Lester

TOP 10: 1987

1. *Stand By Me*
2. *When A Man Loves A Woman*
3. Curiosity Killed The Cat
4. *Male Stripper*
5. Aretha Franklin & George Michael
6. Pepsi & Shirlie
7. Level 42
8. *Live It Up*
9. *Crush On You*
10. Carly Simon

MONTH BY MONTH: 1988

Jan: *All Day And All Of The Night*
Feb: Five

Mar: *Typical Male*
Apr: Eighth Wonder
May: *Lovesexy*
Jun: Jimmy Cliff
Jul: *Breakfast In Bed*
Aug: Tanita Tikaram
Sep: Kevin Saunderson
Oct: *Desire*
Nov: INXS
Dec: *Mistletoe & Wine*

TOP 10: 1988

1. *Orinoco Flow*
2. Kylie Minogue
3. Milli Vanilli
4. Yazz
5. *Kiss*
6. Whitney Houston
7. *We Call It Acieed*
8. Robert Palmer
9. *Wee Rule*
10. Erasure

MONTH BY MONTH: 1989

Jan: *Loco In Acapulco*
Feb: Kym Mazelle
Mar: *Stop*
Apr: Harold Melvin & The Blue Notes
May: Midnight Oil
Jun: Cappella
Jul: The Beautiful South
Aug: Eminem
Sep: Six
Oct: Sydney Youngblood
Nov: Ben Liebrand
Dec: *What The World Is Waiting For*

TOP 10: 1989

1. *Ferry 'Cross The Mersey*
2. Natalie Cole
3. *On The Inside (Theme From 'Prisoner Cell Block H')*
4. Kylie Minogue

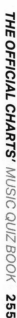

5. Neneh Cherry
6. The London Boys
7. Donna Summer
8. *Bring Me Edelweiss*
9. Bobby Brown
10. Madonna

ONE-WORD NUMBER 1S

1. Dexy's Midnight Runners
2. La Roux
3. Wham!
4. Lily Allen
5. Diana Vickers
6. Telly Savalas
7. Take That
8. Ed Sheeran
9. DJ Fresh featuring Sian Evans
10. Gorillaz
11. John Lennon
12. Deniece Williams
13. Years And Years
14. Dizzee Rascal featuring Armand Van Helden
15. Martin Garrix
16. Ariana Grande
17. Livin' Joy
18. Nelly featuring Kelly Rowland
19. Don McLean
20. Ken Dodd
21. Shakespears Sister
22. Christina Aguilera
23. Brotherhood Of Man
24. Frankie Goes To Hollywood
25. Iyaz
26. Stereophonics
27. Charles Aznavour
28. Calvin Harris featuring John Newman
29. U2
30. Gabrielle
31. The Jam
32. Gary Numan
33. Internet Money featuring Don Toliver, Gunna and Nav
34. David Guetta featuring Sia
35. Robbie Williams
36. Clean Bandit featuring Zara Larsson
37. Peter Andre
38. Petula Clark
39. Pussycat
40. Madonna

CALLING YOUR NAME

1. Bjork
2. Adele
3. Seal
4. Madonna
5. Eve
6. Sting
7. Dido
8. Shanice
9. Donovan
10. Robyn
11. Sia
12. Akon
13. Enya
14. Usher
15. Martika
16. Moby
17. Mabel
18. Shakira
19. Beck
20. Aaliyah

NOW THAT'S WHAT I CALL AN OPENER

1. *The Only Way Is Up*
2. *Baby Come Back*
3. *Reet Petite*
4. *If Tomorrow Never Comes*
5. *Always On My Mind*
6. *Havana*
7. *Grenade*
8. *You Can't Hurry Love*
9. *Somebody That I Used To Know*
10. *Rise*
11. *Somebody To Love*

12. *The Reflex*
13. *The Promise*
14. *Wannabe*
15. *Sleeping Satellite*
16. *With A Little Help From My Friends*
17. *Ghost*
18. *Push The Button*
19. *Toxic*
20. *Someone Like You*

YOU'RE SPEAKING MY LANGUAGE

1. Los Lobos
2. Sash!
3. Manhattan Transfer
4. Kraftwerk
5. Sarah Brightman and Paul Miles-Kingston
6. Jimmy Somerville with June Miles-Kingston
7. Ofra Haza
8. Celine Dion
9. O-Zone
10. Sylvia
11. Alizee
12. Jane Birkin and Serge Gainsbourg
13. Panjabi MC
14. Steeleye Span
15. Mory Kante
16. Plastic Bertrand
17. The Sandpipers
18. Luciano Pavarotti
19. The Singing Nun
20. Sergio Mendes featuring The Black Eyed Peas

HIT AFTER HIT / ONE TO FIVE

Billy Ocean: e-a-c-b-d
Tom Jones: d-e-a-c-b

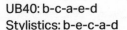

HIT AFTER HIT / ONE TO FIVE

UB40: b-c-a-e-d
Stylistics: b-e-c-a-d

NAME AND NUMBER

1. The B-52's
2. 50 Cent
3. S Club 7
4. UB40
5. Blink-182
6. Unit Four Plus Two
7. 3 Of A Kind
8. Level 42
9. The 1975
10. Apollo 440
11. The 49ers
12. Sum 41
13. 5 Seconds Of Summer
14. Energy 52
15. Sham 69
16. Heaven 17
17. K7
18. Altern 8
19. G4
20. U2

SUPERSTAR SPOTLIGHT: KATE BUSH

1. 44 years: March 1978 to June 2022
2. *Don't Give Up*
3. *Never For Ever*
4. *Rocket Man*
5. *King Of the Mountain*
6. d-a-c-e-b

WHO'S DAVID?

1. David Soul
2. David Gray
3. David Bowie
4. Dave
5. David Essex
6. David Whitfield

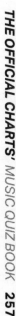

7. David Cassidy
8. Dave Berry
9. David Joseph
10. David Ruffin
11. David Zowie
12. David Parton
13. David Lee Roth
14. David Sneddon
15. Dave Edmunds
16. David Grant
17. Dave Davies
18. David Sylvian
19. David Dundas
20. The Dave Brubeck Quartet

SAME TITLE, DIFFERENT SONGS

1. *Hello*
2. *Freedom*
3. *Happy Birthday*
4. *Perfect*
5. *Wings*
6. *Open Your Heart*
7. *All The Things She Said*
8. *Something About You*
9. *Happy*
10. *Paradise*
11. *Crazy*
12. *I Want Your Love*
13. *Crazy For You*
14. *Falling*
15. *Heartbeat*
16. *Is This Love*
17. *Star*
18. *Maneater*
19. *Stomp*
20. *Get Down*
21. *Angel*
22. *Changes*
23. *Hold On*
24. *Breakout*
25. *Stay*
26. *Mirrors*
27. *Be My Baby*
28. *Rockstar*

29. *Runaway*
30. *Take A Chance On Me*
31. *Don't Stop The Music*
32. *Don't Stop Movin'*
33. *Don't Worry*
34. *All Around The World*
35. *Fly Away*
36. *Wishing Well*
37. *Come As You Are*
38. *I Won't Let You Down*
39. *Walking On Sunshine*
40. *Waves*

HIT AFTER HIT / ONE TO FIVE

Robbie Williams: b-a-c-d-e
Frank Sinatra: d-b-a-c-e

I KNOW WHAT I LIKE (IN YOUR WARDROBE)

1. Madness
2. Bombalurina
3. Jimmy Nail
4. The View
5. Stereophonics
6. Justin Timberlake featuring Jay-Z
7. Prince and The Revolution
8. Shontelle
9. Haircut One Hundred
10. Kenny
11. Jonny Trunk And Wisbey
12. Sisqo
13. Roxy Music
14. Taylor Swift
15. Patrick MacNee & Honor Blackman
16. St. Cecilia
17. Sandie Shaw
18. The Wedding Present
19. Paul Young
20. Sugababes

SUPERSTAR SPOTLIGHT: ABBA

1. 1974
2. Nine
3. Cilla Black
4. Eight
5. *The Name Of The Game*
6. b-a-e-d-c

HIT AFTER HIT / ONE TO FIVE

Genesis: b-e-c-a-d
U2: a-e-b-c-d

MISSING WORDS

1. *I Don't Need This Pressure On*
2. *However Do You Want Me*
3. *I Believe In Love*
4. *Just Like*
5. *Don't Feel Sorry For Loverboy*
6. *Best That You Can Do*
7. *All Night*
8. *In The Name Of Love*
9. *Give Me Your Heart*
10. *Who Loves Me*
11. *Clock Of The Heart*
12. *Living It Up*
13. *Mamba Seyra*
14. *Forget About Me*
15. *Gioca Jouer*
16. *Man In Motion*
17. *I Just*
18. *Get Fresh At The Weekend*
19. *Al-Li-Ayo*
20. *Go For It*
21. *Hooked On Love*
22. *Wherever I Go*
23. *Wild One*
24. *Take A Look At Me Now*
25. *Don't Don't Do It*
26. *For My Love*
27. *Like A Record*
28. *Nothing Serious*
29. *500 Miles*
30. *Let's Make Lots Of Money*
31. *Something Inside*
32. *To Bed*
33. *Feels Like*
34. *No Can Do*
35. *If I Had A Photograph Of You*
36. *Doin' Up The House*
37. *400 Miles*
38. *Say So Much*
39. *No More Love On The Run*
40. *On And Off And On Again*

HIT AFTER HIT / ONE TO FIVE

a-ha: c-e-b-a-d
Eurythmics: c-a-d-e-b

GET A LIFE

1. Stevie Wonder
2. Alex Party
3. Billy Joel
4. Inner City
5. Kelly Clarkson
6. Nina Simone
7. Joyce Sims
8. The Gibson Brothers
9. The Tamperer featuring Maya
10. Joe Walsh
11. Cliff Bennett & The Rebel Rousers
12. Dr. Alban
13. Michael Holiday
14. The Fray
15. Opus
16. The Mamalade
17. Boyzone
18. Skid Row
19. Indeep
20. Evanescence

SCOTLAND FOREVER

1. Annie Lennox
2. The Proclaimers
3. Emeli Sande
4. Hue & Cry
5. Aztec Camera
6. KT Tunstall

7. The Jesus & Mary Chain
8. Al Stewart
9. Altered Images
10. Travis
11. Strawberry Switchblade
12. Edwyn Collins
13. Gerry Rafferty
14. The Bluebells
15. Jimmy Somerville
16. Hipsway
17. Barbara Dickson
18. Fish
19. Runrig
20. Sheena Easton

GIRLS, GIRLS, GIRLS

1. Tom Jones
2. Kaiser Chiefs
3. The Rolling Stones
4. Kool & The Gang
5. Barry Ryan
6. Cliff Richard
7. Scissor Sisters
8. Laura Branigan
9. Gilbert O'Sullivan
10. Hot Chocolate
11. Toto
12. John Travolta
13. The Human League
14. The Four Pennies
15. Thin Lizzy
16. Marillion
17. Focus
18. The Art Company
19. Mark Ronson featuring Amy Winehouse
20. Blondie

2 BECOME 1

1. Aretha Franklin / George Michael
2. Shakira / Wyclef Jean
3. Take That / Lulu
4. Olivia Newton-John / Electric Light Orchestra

5. Tinchy Stryder / N-Dubz
6. Lady Gaga / Beyoncé
7. Sugababes / Girls Aloud
8. Paul McCartney / Stevie Wonder
9. Olly Murs / Rizzle Kicks
10. Vic Reeves / The Wonderstuff
11. Sam Smith / John Legend
12. Kylie Minogue / Jason Donovan
13. Rihanna / Calvin Harris
14. Estelle / Kanye West
15. Blue / Elton John
16. Elaine Paige / Barbara Dickson
17. Madonna / Justin Timberlake
18. Will Young / Gareth Gates
19. Rita Ora / Tinie Tempah
20. Mariah Carey / Westlife

SUPERSTAR SPOTLIGHT: GEORGE MICHAEL

1. *Make It Big*
2. *Enjoy What You Do*
3. Three weeks
4. *The Edge Of Heaven*
5. *As*
6. a-e-c-d-b

WHAT'S MY NAME?

1. Freddie Mercury
2. Lady Gaga
3. Cliff Richard
4. Jay-Z
5. Calvin Harris
6. Chaka Khan
7. MC Hammer
8. Kiki Dee
9. 50 Cent
10. Elvis Costello
11. Stormzy
12. Cher
13. Pitbull
14. Lizzo
15. Bruno Mars

16. Eninem
17. Lorde
18. The Weeknd
19. Shaggy
20. Snoop Dogg

HIT AFTER HIT / ONE TO FIVE

Erasure: b-d-a-c-e
Jason Derulo: c-b-e-a-d

NUL POINTS

1. Sandie Shaw
2. Scooch
3. Lulu
4. Jemini
5. Bardo
6. Lynsey de Paul and Mike Moran
7. Imaani
8. Javine
9. Olivia Newton-John
10. Belle & The Devotions
11. Ronnie Carroll
12. Clodagh Rodgers
13. Daz Sampson
14. The Shadows
15. Blue
16. The Allisons
17. Jessica Garlick
18. Sonia
19. Co-Co
20. Michael Ball

HIT AFTER HIT / ONE TO FIVE

Blondie: b-c-a-d-e
Adam & The Ants: e-a-d-c-b

MONTH BY MONTH: 1990

Jan: Jimmy Somerville
Feb: Walk On By
Mar: Alannah Myles
Apr: Penny Lane
May: The Family Stand
Jun: Venus
Jul: Bob Geldof
Aug: Pretty Woman
Sep: I'll Never Fall In Love Again
Oct: Blue Velvet
Nov: Kim Appleby
Dec: Wicked Game

TOP 10: 1990

1. Turtle Power
2. Madonna
3. Tom's Diner
4. Elton John
5. MC Hammer
6. Naked In The Rain
7. Mona
8. I'm Free
9. Technotronic featuring Ya Kid K
10. Roxette

MONTH BY MONTH: 1991

Jan: Jesus Jones
Feb: How Soon Is Now
Mar: Dina Carroll
Apr: The Bee Gees
May: Electronic
Jun: Kate Pierson
Jul: Cola Boy
Aug: True
Sep: Arnee And The Terminators
Oct: Julian Lennon
Nov: It's Grim Up North
Dec: Kym Sims

TOP 10: 1991

1. U2
2. Dizzy
3. 2 Unlimited
4. Bryan Adams
5. World In Union
6. Wind Of Change
7. Always Look On The Bright Side Of Life

8. Oceanic
9. Genesis
10. Moby

MONTH BY MONTH: 1992

Jan: Bjork
Feb: Opus III
Mar: Vanessa Williams
Apr: Senseless Things
May: *Beauty And The Beast*
Jun: *The Abba-esque EP*
Jul: Kim Basinger & Ozzy Osbourne
Aug: Jon Secada
Sep: *House Of Love*
Oct: Lionel Richie
Nov: 1983
Dec: The Shamen

TOP 10: 1992

1. KWS
2. *On A Ragga Tip*
3. Curiosity
4. 2 Unlimited
5. *Deeply Dippy*
6. Marc Almond
7. Metallica
8. En Vogue
9. Curtis Stigers
10. The Wedding Present

MONTH BY MONTH: 1993

Jan: Faith No More
Feb: The Beloved
Mar: *Cat's In The Cradle*
Apr: Bill Tarmey
May: House Of Pain
Jun: Spin Doctors
Jul: *Pray*
Aug: Urban Cookie Collective
Sep: Village People
Oct: *Fairground* by Simply Red
Nov: Soul Asylum
Dec: *Mr Blobby* by Mr Blobby

TOP 10: 1993

1. *Young At Heart*
2. *Informer*
3. *Ain't No Love (Ain't No Use)*
4. New Order
5. Sybil
6. Cappella
7. *Don't Walk Away*
8. Shaggy
9. Whitney Houston
10. *Show Me Love*

MONTH BY MONTH: 1994

Jan: Tori Amos
Feb: Aretha Franklin
Mar: Morrissey
Apr: *The Most Beautiful Girl In The World*
May: Stiltskin
Jun: Soft Cell (the song was *Tainted Love*)
Jul: Gun
Aug: 1974
Sep: Phil Daniels
Oct: *The Lion King*
Nov: *Spin The Black Circle*
Dec: Zig & Zag

TOP 10: 1994

1. *Love Is All Around*
2. Let Loose
3. *Compliments On Your Kiss*
4. *7 Seconds*
5. China Black
6. All-4-One
7. *What's Up*
8. *Regulate*
9. Tinmen
10. Oasis

MONTH BY MONTH: 1995

Jan: Rednex
Feb: *Riverdance*
Mar: Scarlet
Apr: *Chains*
May: *Cherry Pink And Apple Blossom White*
Jun: Michael & Janet Jackson
Jul: *I'm A Believer*
Aug: The Connells
Sep: Elkie Brooks
Oct: Nick Cave
Nov: L.V.
Dec: *Wonderwall*

TOP 10: 1995

1. The Outhere Brothers
2. *Love Can Build A Bridge*
3. Wet Wet Wet
4. Celine Dion
5. Bobby Brown
6. *U Sure Do*
7. The Beatles
8. Alex Party
9. *Turn On, Tune In, Cop Out*
10. East 17

MONTH BY MONTH: 1996

Jan: Cast
Feb: *I Just Want To Make Love To You*
Mar: Garbage
Apr: Mark Snow
May: *Nobody Knows*
Jun: Bubbler Ranx
Jul: Alison Limerick
Aug: Paul Weller
Sep: *Ready Or Not*
Oct: *Breakfast At Tiffanys*
Nov: Reef
Dec: Maria Nayler

TOP 10: 1996

1. George Michael
2. Mark Morrison
3. Gina G
4. Manic Street Preachers
5. *Cecilia*
6. Michael Jackson
7. Pet Shop Boys
8. Manchester United Football Club
9. *Keep On Jumpin'*
10. Sleeper

MONTH BY MONTH: 1997

Jan: White Town
Feb: The Orb
Mar: *You Got The Love* by The Source featuring *Candi Staton*
Apr: *You Showed Me*
May: *Drop Dead Gorgeous*
Jun: *I Want You*
Jul: Gala
Aug: *California Dreaming*
Sep: Betley Rhythm Ace
Oct: *Something About The Way You Look Tonight*
Nov: Ewan McGregor
Dec: Boyzone

TOP 10: 1997

1. *MmmBop*
2. *I Wanna Be The Only One*
3. Radiohead
4. *Time To Say Goodbye*
5. *Closer Than Close*
6. *You're Not Alone*
7. *I'll Be There For You*
8. The Cardigans
9. Sneaker Pimps
10. *Waltz Away Dreaming*

MONTH BY MONTH: 1998

Jan: *Get Down Tonight*
Feb: Aaron Carter
Mar: Love Affair
Apr: Daniel O'Donnell
May: Cocteau Twins
Jun: Des'ree
Jul: *Deeper Underground*
Aug: Stardust
Sep: *Millennium*
Oct: Alanis Morissette
Nov: Touch & Go
Dec: *Goodbye*

TOP 10: 1998

1. *Gym & Tonic*
2. 911
3. Billie
4. B*Witched
5. *I Don't Want To Miss A Thing*
6. R.E.M.
7. Fatboy Slim
8. The Beautiful South
9. *How Deep Is Your Love*
10. Cliff Richard

MONTH BY MONTH: 1999

Jan: Tony Christie
Feb: The Divine Comedy
Mar: *Lullaby*
Apr: New Radicals
May: *Swear It Again*
Jun: *Beautiful Stranger*
Jul: *Secret Smile*
Aug: Bran Van 3000
Sep: Sixpence None The Richer
Oct: *Genie In A Bottle*
Nov: *Keep On Movin'*
Dec: Len

TOP 10: 1999

1. Vengaboys
2. *Mambo No.5 (A Little Bit Of...)*
3. *DJ Jean*
4. Lolly
5. *Friends Forever*
6. Shaft
7. *Afrika Shox*
8. Enrique Iglesias
9. Supergrass
10. Martine McCutcheon

SENSES WORKING OVERTIME

1. Nirvana
2. The Who
3. MC Hammer
4. Aitch
5. KT Tunstall
6. Genesis
7. The Three Degrees
8. King
9. Marvin Gaye
10. The Bloodhound Gang
11. Pink Floyd
12. Little Mix
13. Jon & Vangelis
14. Johnny Nash
15. Samantha Fox
16. Dave Edmunds
17. Jamelia
18. Divinyls
19. The Move
20. Depeche Mode

INSTRUMENTAL HITS

1. Vangelis
2. The Brighouse and Rastrick Brass Band
3. The Pipes And Drums And Military Band Of The Royal Scots Dragoon Guards
4. Jan Hammer
5. Ennio Morricone
6. The Shadows

7. 808 State
8. Floyd Cramer
9. Mike Oldfield
10. Sandy Nelson
11. Harold Faltermeyer
12. Mason Williams
13. Percy Faith
14. Orbital
15. Horst Jankowski
16. Violinski
17. Mezzoforte
18. Space
19. David A. Stewart and Candy Dulfer
20. Jean-Michel Jarre

HIT AFTER HIT / ONE TO FIVE

Muse: a-c-e-b-d
Shirley Bassey: a-c-d-e-b

UNLUCKY FOR SOME

1. Joy Division
2. T Rex
3. Aerosmith
4. Gloria Gaynor
5. Alcazar
6. Air
7. Diana Ross
8. Republica
9. Simple Minds
10. Portishead
11. Boz Scaggs
12. Sophie B. Hawkins
13. James Brown And The Famous Flames
14. Loose Ends
15. Del Amitri
16. Jocelyn Brown
17. Tone Loc
18. The S.O.S. Band
19. AC/DC
20. Roxy Music

WHERE THEM GIRLS AT?

1. Atomic Kitten
2. All Saints
3. Girls Aloud
4. TLC
5. Hepburn
6. Honeyz
7. Mis-Teeq
8. Spice Girls
9. Destiny's Child
10. Precious
11. Jade
12. Eternal
13. Buffalo G
14. SWV
15. Bellefire
16. En Vogue
17. Girl Thing
18. Cleopatra
19. B*Witched
20. Sugababes

HIT AFTER HIT / ONE TO FIVE

Five Star: d-e-a-b-c
Ellie Goulding: e-d-b-c-a

HIT AFTER HIT / ONE TO FIVE

Jason Donovan: c-a-b-e-d
P!nk: e-d-c-b-a

NUMBER 11 HITS

1. Stevie Wonder
2. Blur
3. John Travolta
4. Blondie
5. Joni Mitchell
6. Big Audio Dynamite
7. Red Hot Chili Peppers
8. Simply Red
9. Joan Armatrading
10. Andrew Gold
11. Robert Plant
12. Oasis

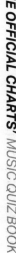

13. Fountains Of Wayne
14. Spice Girls
15. INXS
16. Mama Cass with The Mamas & The Papas
17. Rod Stewart
18. The Bangles
19. Alanis Morissette
20. Idina Menzel

SUPERSTAR SPOTLIGHT: QUEEN & FREDDIE MERCURY

1. *Seven Seas Of Rhye*
2. *One Vision*
3. *These Are The Days Of Our Lives*
4. Just three – *Bohemian Rhapsody* on its initial release in 1975 *Under Pressure* with David Bowie in 1981 and *Innuendo* was the final one in 1991
5. *Love Kills*
6. d-e-b-a-c

HIT AFTER HIT / ONE TO FIVE

Iron Maiden: a-e-d-b-c
Status Quo: c-a-b-e-d

FOR THOSE ABOUT TO ROCK (WE SALUTE YOU)

1. Bon Jovi
2. Status Quo
3. The Jimi Hendrix Experience
4. Led Zeppelin
5. Guns N' Roses
6. Motörhead
7. Iron Maiden
8. The Who
9. Judas Priest
10. Metallica
11. Slipknot
12. Rainbow
13. Free
14. Green Day
15. Deep Purple
16. Cream
17. Queen
18. Van Halen
19. Sex Pistols
20. Foo Fighters
21. The Rolling Stones
22. Black Sabbath
23. Kiss
24. AC/DC
25. ZZ Top
26. The Clash
27. Nirvana
28. Genesis
29. Paramore
30. Red Hot Chili Peppers
31. Thin Lizzy
32. U2
33. Linkin Park
34. Pearl Jam
35. Motley Crue
36. Faith No More
37. Whitesnake
38. Jane's Addiction
39. Def Leppard
40. Aerosmith

HIT AFTER HIT / ONE TO FIVE

Bon Jovi: b-e-d-a-c
Bryan Adams: c-d-b-e-a

MADE IN WALES

1. Tom Jones
2. Shakin' Stevens
3. Stereophonics
4. Aled Jones
5. Shirley Bassey
6. Manic Street Preachers
7. Harry Secombe
8. Super Furry Animals
9. Catatonia
10. Mary Hopkin
11. Jem
12. Donna Lewis

13. Duffy
14. Dave Edmunds
15. Goldie Looking Chain
16. The Alarm
17. Ricky Valance
18. Charlotte Church
19. Badfinger
20. Bonnie Tyler

SUPERSTAR SPOTLIGHT: OASIS

1. *Supersonic*
2. Death In Vegas
3. *Roll With It*
4. *The Death Of You And Me*
5. *Falling Down*
6. *d-e-a-c-b*

HIT AFTER HIT / ONE TO FIVE

Spice Girls a-e-d-c-b
Backstreet Boys: c-d-e-a-b

I'LL BE MISSING YOU

1. *But I Won't Do That*
2. *For A White Guy*
3. *We Want*
4. *Da Funk*
5. *Get Wicked*
6. *Wiggle Wiggle*
7. *Without A Woman*
8. *I Wanna Give You*
9. *A La La La La Long*
10. *Before The Night Is Over*
11. *Con Te Partiro*
12. *Waltzing Matilda*
13. *Start The Dance*
14. *Fade Out*
15. *Mucho Mambo*
16. *The Postman Song*
17. *Ain't No Use*
18. *Time Of Your Life*
19. *All Night Long*
20. *Tears From My Eyes*
21. *Take A Little*
22. *These Sounds Fall Into My Mind*

23. *There It Is*
24. *Ski-Ba-Bop-Ba-Dop-Bop*
25. *To Wear Sunscreen*
26. *No, No, No*
27. *For The Love Of A Princess*
28. *Un, Dos, Tres*
29. *I Missed You*
30. *That Thing*
31. *Turn Your Radio On*
32. *Till I Come*
33. *It's Got To Be Big*
34. *I'm Coming Back*
35. *Ghetto Anthem*
36. *The Vengabus*
37. *That's The Way Life Is*
38. *That Is What You Are*
39. *Backstreet's Back*
40. *The Crowd Say Bo Selecta*

HIT AFTER HIT / ONE TO FIVE

Take That: b-a-c-e-d
Westlife: a-d-e-c-b

AROUND THE WORLD

1. Coldplay & Rihanna
2. Vengaboys
3. Kirsty MacColl
4. Kim Wilde
5. Julie Covington
6. Childish Gambino
7. Gibson Brothers
8. Fireboy DML & Ed Sheeran
9. Alphaville
10. Umboza
11. DJ Khaled featuring Drake
12. Bonnie Tyler
13. Bennet
14. The Future Sound Of London
15. Human League
16. Mitchell Torok
17. Sash! featuring Rodriguez
18. Manhattan Transfer
19. Typically Tropical
20. Manic Street Preachers

DON'T LET IT SHOW ON YOUR FACE

1. Lady Gaga
2. The Weeknd
3. Roberta Flack
4. Billy Idol
5. Andy Why Not?
6. Little Richard
7. 2 Unlimited
8. Paul McCartney
9. Marti Webb
10. Dream Warriors
11. Stephanie De Sykes And Rain
12. Maroon 5 featuring Rihanna
13. 808 State
14. Sham 69
15. Siouxsie And The Banshees
16. Louise
17. Gnarls Barkley
18. The Glitter Band
19. The Monks
20. Joe Dolce Music Theatre

SOMETHING IN COMMON

1. Jackson
2. Collins
3. John
4. Jones
5. White
6. Anderson
7. Moore
8. Brown
9. Smith
10. Stewart
11. Lewis
12. Williams
13. Grant
14. Young
15. Stevens
16. Thomas
17. Johnson
18. Walker
19. Martin
20. Miller

TAKE ME TO THE HOSPITAL

1. P!nk
2. Elton John
3. Ne-Yo
4. Peggy Lee
5. Thompson Twins
6. The Jam
7. Bon Jovi
8. Madness
9. Ed Sheeran and Rudimental
10. D 12
11. Dr Dre featuring Eminem & Skylar Grey
12. PM Dawn
13. Ultra Nate
14. Sunny
15. Depeche Mode
16. Mylo Vs Miami Sound Machine
17. Editors
18. The Smiths
19. Sky & Robbie featuring Simply Red
20. Aqua

SUPERSTAR SPOTLIGHT: MICHAEL JACKSON

1. 1970
2. *Show You The Way To Go*
3. Four (*Don't Stop 'Til You Get Enough, Off The Wall, Rock With You, She's Out Of My Life*)
4. Number 10
5. *Earth Song*
6. e-a-b-d-c

FOOD FOR THOUGHT

1. Harry Styles
2. Hot Butter
3. Kelis
4. The Rolling Stones
5. Booker T & The MG's
6. The Dickies

7. Prince And The New
   Power Generation
8. Streetband
9. Mariah Carey
10. The Searchers
11. The Presidents Of
    The United States
12. Kylie Minogue
13. BTS
14. The Carpenters
15. Stephen 'Tin Tin' Duffy
16. Drake
17. The Mudlarks
18. The Newbeats
19. Galantis
20. Spitting Image

HIT AFTER HIT / ONE TO FIVE

Jamiroquai: d-a-c-b-e
Rihanna: e-d-b-a-c

ANYONE WHO HAD A HEART

1. Bonnie Tyler
2. Deee-Lite
3. Blondie
4. Nick Kamen
5. Celine Dion
6. Neil Young
7. Mark Ronson And Miley Cyrus
8. Billy Ray Cyrus
9. Survivor
10. Gallagher & Lyle
11. Aztec Camera
12. Squeeze
13. Toni Braxton
14. ABC
15. The Three Degrees
16. Taylor Dayne
17. James Blunt
18. Dua Lipa
19. Dollar
20. Feargal Sharkey

HIT AFTER HIT / ONE TO FIVE

Boyzone c-a-b-e-d
Ronan Keating: a-d-b-c-e

MONTH BY MONTH: 2000

Jan: *The Masses Against
The Classes*
Feb: R.E.M.
Mar: Beenie Man
Apr: Lisa 'Left Eye' Lopes
May: *Candy*
Jun: George Michael
Jul: *Breathless*
Aug: Finnish
Sep: Sugababes
Oct: *Who Let The Dogs Out*
Nov: The Tweenies
Dec: *Can We Fix It*

TOP 10: 2000

1. Geri Halliwell
2. Bink-182
3. *Don't Give Up*
4. ATB
5. Madonna
6. *Still Dre*
7. All Saints
8. *Sitting Down Here*
9. *Mama Told Me Not To Come*
10. Vengaboys

MONTH BY MONTH: 2001

Jan: *Rollin'*
Feb: Dido
Mar: *Nobody Wants To Be Lonely*
Apr: Missy Elliott
May: 1984
Jun: *Electric Avenue*
Jul: Ian Van Dahl
Aug: Lisa Maffia
Sep: Stealers Wheel
Oct: Liberty
Nov: *Closer To Me*
Dec: Kate Winslet

ANSWERS

THE OFFICIAL CHARTS' *MUSIC QUIZ BOOK* **269**

TOP 10: 2001

1. *Another Chance*
2. *Lady Marmalade*
3. Wheatus
4. *Heaven Is A Halfpipe*
5. Hear'Say
6. Usher
7. *Angel*
8. Faith Hill
9. Gorillaz
10. Mis-Teeq

MONTH BY MONTH: 2002

Jan: *Gotta Get Thru This*
Feb: *Crazy Rap*
Mar: *Anything Is Possible*
Apr: Shaggy
May: *How You Remind Me*
Jun: 1979
Jul: Alessandro Safina
Aug: *Colourblind*
Sep: Kelly Osbourne
Oct: *Bunsen Burner*
Nov: DJ Sammy & Yanou
        featuring Do
Dec: *Escapology*

TOP 10: 2002

1. *Hero*
2. P!nk
3. A1
4. Britney Spears
5. *Addicted To Bass*
6. Ja Rule featuring Ashanti
7. *True Love Never Dies*
8. George Harrison
9. Christina Milian
10. Kaci

MONTH BY MONTH: 2003

Jan: Peter Gabriel
Feb: *Lifestyles Of The
        Rich & Famous*

Mar: 1970
Apr: Coldplay
May: Steps
Jun: Electric Six
Jul: *Pass It On*
Aug: Pretty Green Eyes
Sep: The Darkness
Oct: *Say Cheese (Smile Please)*
Nov: Blazin' Squad
Dec: 1985

TOP 10: 2003

1. *Loneliness*
2. *Rise & Fall*
3. Ronan Keating
4. *You Said No*
5. Kelly Rowland
6. *All Over*
7. 50 Cent
8. *X Gon Give It To Ya*
9. *Make Luv*
10. David Sneddon

MONTH BY MONTH: 2004

Jan: Kelis
Feb: *How Will I Know*
Mar: JLS
Apr: *Through The Wire*
May: Frankee
Jun: Emma Bunton
Jul: The Ones
Aug: *Can't Stand Me Now*
Sep: Brian McFadden
Oct: Andrea True Connection
Nov: *My Prerogative*
Dec: Chris Martin

TOP 10: 2004

1. McFly
2. *Yeah*
3. *In The Shadows*
4. Anastacia
5. *Cha Cha Slide*
6. *Come With Me*

7. *Slow Jamz*
8. Blue
9. *I Like It*
10. Beyoncé

MONTH BY MONTH: 2005

Jan: Athlete
Feb: U2
Mar: *Hounds Of Love*
Apr: Natalie Imbruglia
May: *Lyla*
Jun: 1985
Jul: Charlotte Church
Aug: *Back To Bedlam*
Sep: Simon Webbe
Oct: *Nine Million Bicycles*
Nov: *Gimme, Gimme, Gimme (A Man After Midnight)*
Dec: Nizlopi

TOP 10: 2005

1. Sugababes
2. Robbie Williams
3. *Don't Cha*
4. Depeche Mode
5. Sean Paul
6. *Gold Digger*
7. Bloc Party
8. Liberty X
9. Mariah Carey
10. *Bad Day*

MONTH BY MONTH: 2006

Jan: Arctic Monkeys
Feb: 1977
Mar: *Put Your Records On*
Apr: Nine
May: The White Stripes
Jun: The Automatic
Jul: *Don't Stop Me Now*
Aug: James Morrison
Sep: The Feeling
Oct: *Breaking Free*
Nov: Take That

Dec: Soundgarden

TOP 10: 2006

1. *Welcome To The Black Parade*
2. Razorlight
3. *Scissor Sisters*
4. *Rock This Party (Everybody Dance Now)*
5. *Come To Me*
6. Lil' Chris
7. Beatfreakz
8. The Killers
9. Justin Timberlake
10. *Jump In My Car*

MONTH BY MONTH: 2007

Jan: Just Jack
Feb: *The Sweet Escape*
Mar: Calvin Harris
Apr: *I Wanna Have Your Babies*
May: Nina Persson
Jun: Mutya Buena
Jul: *Worried About Ray*
Aug: Green Day
Sep: Babyshambles
Oct: Joy Division
Nov: Seven
Dec: Whitney Houston & Mariah Carey

TOP 10: 2007

1. *Beautiful Girls*
2. *Hey There Delilah*
3. Kanye West
4. James Blunt
5. *Ayo Technology*
6. Rihanna
7. Girls Aloud
8. *With Every Heartbeat*
9. *The Way I Are*
10. Scouting For Girls

MONTH BY MONTH: 2008

Jan: *Chasing Pavements*
Feb: Hot Chip
Mar: Rockferry
Apr: *Fascination*
May: *Propane Nightmares*
Jun: Sheila B. Devotion
Jul: Ironik
Aug: *I Kissed A Girl*
Sep: Cliff Richard
Oct: Peter Kay
Nov: *Day & Age*
Dec: Jeff Buckley

TOP 10: 2008

1. Ne-Yo
2. Coldplay
3. *No Air*
4. *Forever*
5. Rihanna
6. *Love Song*
7. Gabriella Cilmi
8. The Ting Tings
9. Duffy
10. *We Made It*

MONTH BY MONTH: 2009

Jan: *Just Dance*
Feb: *World In Motion* by Englandneworder
Mar: *Gavin & Stacey*
Apr: *In For The Kill*
May: Norway
Jun: Kelly Rowland
Jul: JLS
Aug: Michael Jackson
Sep: *I Left My Heart In Tokyo*
Oct: New York
Nov: Ke$ha
Dec: 1993

TOP 10: 2009

1. Chipmunk
2. The Saturdays
3. *Empire State Of Mind*
4. Taio Cruz
5. *Sexy Bitch (aka Sexy Chick)*
6. *Sweet Disposition*
7. Shakira
8. Black Eyed Peas
9. Pitbull
10. *Run This Town*

LIVING FOR THE CITY

1. Ultravox
2. Little Jimmy Osmond
3. Freddie Mercury & Montserrat Caballe
4. Duran Duran
5. Winifred Atwell
6. Fedde Le Grand
7. Scott McKenzie
8. Madness
9. Murray Head
10. Crosby Stills & Nash
11. Bryan Ferry
12. Kenny Ball & His Jazzmen
13. Mott The Hoople
14. Boney M
15. The Mobiles
16. Elvis Presley
17. The Sensational Alex Harvey Band
18. The Pogues & Kirsty MacColl
19. Bruce Springsteen
20. Gladys Knight & The Pips

BURN IT UP

1. The Prodigy
2. Alicia Keys
3. Glenn Frey
4. Jerry Lee Lewis
5. Ellie Goulding
6. Stevie Nicks

7. Julie Driscoll & The Brian Auger Trinity
8. The Power Station
9. U2
10. Mimi Webb
11. Tom Jones & The Cardigans
12. Nelly
13. Bucks Fizz
14. 5000 Volts
15. Ash
16. The Crazy World Of Arthur Brown
17. The Ruts
18. The Platters
19. Donna Summer
20. Billy Joel

REGGAE FOR IT NOW

1. Althia & Donna
2. Desmond Dekker
3. Barry Biggs
4. Janet Kay
5. Dave & Ansil Collins
6. John Holt
7. Harry J All-Stars
8. Jimmy Cliff
9. Nicky Thomas
10. Sophia George
11. Junior Murvin
12. Dandy Livingstone
13. The Pioneers
14. Freddie McGregor
15. Black Slate
16. Dennis Brown
17. Susan Cadogan
18. Errol Dunkley
19. Pluto Shervington
20. Bob And Marcia

BE YOUNG, BE FOOLISH, BE HAPPY

1. Pharrell Williams
2. The Housemartins
3. Britney Spears

4. Mika
5. Bobby McFerrin
6. The Who
7. Avril Lavigne
8. Siouxsie And The Banshees
9. The Edwin Hawkins Singers
10. Sheryl Crow
11. The Buzzcocks
12. The Turtles
13. Bjork
14. Hot Chocolate
15. Neil Sedaka
16. Michelle Gayle
17. Demis Roussos
18. Altered Images
19. Slim Whitman
20. Captain Sensible

CHART DOUBLES

1. The Beatles
2. Bryan Adams
3. Ed Sheeran
4. The Police
5. Scissor Sisters
6. Elvis Presley
7. Stormzy
8. Madonna
9. Celine Dion
10. Limp Bizkit
11. Miley Cyrus
12. Men At Work
13. Rihanna
14. Drake
15. Sam Smith
16. Wet Wet Wet
17. Olly Murs
18. Atomic Kitten
19. Right Said Fred
20. Barbra Streisand

HIT AFTER HIT / ONE TO FIVE

One Direction: e-a-d-c-b
Girls Aloud: a-d-e-b-c

HIT AFTER HIT / ONE TO FIVE

Depeche Mode: e-a-d-b-c
The Prodigy: b-e-a-c-d

GOING DOWN TO LIVERPOOL

1. Orchestral Manoeuvres In The Dark
2. The Farm
3. The Teardrop Explodes
4. Black
5. The La's
6. Echo & The Bunnymen
7. Holly Johnson
8. Melanic C
9. The Lotus Eaters
10. Rebecca Ferguson
11. The Christians
12. China Crisis
13. Cilla Black
14. The Icicle Works
15. The Zutons
16. Pete Wylie
17. It's Immaterial
18. The Coral
19. A Flock Of Seagulls
20. The Reynolds Girls

SUPERSTAR SPOTLIGHT: KYLIE MINOGUE

1. 13
2. Keith Washington
3. *Tears On My Pillow*
4. Eleven
5. Paula Abdul
6. a-b-c-e-d

FOOTY HITS

1. Baddiel And Skinner And The Lightning Seeds
2. Manchester United Football Squad
3. Kevin Keegan
4. Scotland World Cup Squad
5. Chelsea Football Team
6. Everton 1985
7. Collapsed Lung
8. Glenn & Chris
9. 4-4-2
10. Atomic Kitten
11. West Ham United Cup Squad
12. Cockerel Chorus
13. Bell & Spurling
14. Arsenal FC
15. Liverpool Football Team
16. James Fox And Cardiff City FC
17. Nottingham Forest And Paper Lace
18. Del Amitri
19. Ant & Dec
20. Fat Les

HIT AFTER HIT / ONE TO FIVE

Pet Shop Boys: b-e-c-d-a
McFly: c-a-e-b-d

LONG HOT SUMMER

1. Mungo Jerry
2. Don Henley
3. Kid Rock
4. Cliff Richard and The Shadows
5. DJ Jazzy Jeff and The Fresh Prince
6. Jerry Keller
7. Demi Lovato
8. Danny Wilson
9. Bay City Rollers
10. The Lovin' Spoonful
11. Bananarama
12. The Isley Brothers
13. Lana Del Rey vs Cedric Gervais
14. The Alarm
15. John Travolta and Olivia Newton-John
16. Dodgy
17. Michael Jackson

18. Bobby Goldsboro
19. Lonyo
20. ABBA

GOING MISSING

1. *Is This The Way To*
2. *Put A Ring On It*
3. *Touch My Bum*
4. *If This Ain't Love*
5. *With Flowers In My Hair*
6. *In Your Arms*
7. *You Know I Love You*
8. *Asereje*
9. *Praise You*
10. *Stupid Mistake*
11. *Lick It*
12. *Hear Me Tonight*
13. *Way With*
14. *You Are Beautiful*
15. *Uh Oooh, Uh Oooh*
16. *Casualty*
17. *Get Out*
18. *You Are My Destiny*
19. *Go Baby Go*
20. *Come To An End*

SUPERSTAR SPOTLIGHT: CALVIN HARRIS

1. 2007
2. John Newman
3. *We Found Love*
4. Nine
5. *Dance Wiv Me*
6. c-b-a-e-d

HIT AFTER HIT / ONE TO FIVE

Kanye West: d-a-b-e-c
Jennifer Lopez: b-c-d-e-a

WOMANKIND

1. Shania Twain
2. Cliff Richard
3. Roy Orbison

4. Kate Bush
5. Don Williams
6. Britney Spears
7. Stevie Wonder
8. Doja Cat
9. Gabrielle
10. Deep Purple
11. Barbra Streisand
12. Joe Tex
13. Little Mix featuring Nicki Minaj
14. Mud
15. Marvin Rainwater
16. Mungo Jerry
17. Eternal
18. Electric Light Orchestra
19. Ariana Grande
20. Tears For Fears

BOYS WILL BE BOYS

1. Boyzone
2. Blue
3. Take That
4. *NSYNC
5. MN8
6. Another Level
7. Backstreet Boys
8. Upside Down
9. Busted
10. Bad Boys Inc.
11. O-Town
12. Five
13. North And South
14. Westlife
15. Phixx
16. Color Me Badd
17. Damage
18. A1
19. New Kids On The Block
20. East 17

HIT AFTER HIT / ONE TO FIVE

East 17: b-e-d-c-a
911: a-e-b-e-c

TELL ME WHEN

1. Ronan Keating
2. Johnny Mathis
3. ABC
4. Prefab Sprout
5. Janet Jackson
6. Arctic Monkeys
7. Bruno Mars
8. Matt Terry
9. Demis Roussos
10. Pussycat Dolls
11. The Marvelettes
12. The Four Tops
13. Sybil
14. Leo Sayer
15. Tina Turner
16. Jason Donovan
17. Bucks Fizz
18. White Plains
19. Diana Ross
20. David Guetta featuring Kelly Rowland

REGAL HITS

1. Queen
2. Adam & The Ants
3. Stevie Wonder
4. Prefab Sprout
5. ABBA
6. Years & Years
7. Spin Doctors
8. Fetty Wap
9. Elvis Presley
10. Madness
11. KC & The Sunshine Band
12. Roger Miller
13. Darts
14. Westlife
15. Stranglers
16. China Crisis
17. Dave Edmunds
18. Ed Sheeran
19. Wamdue Project
20. Sex Pistols

HIT AFTER HIT / ONE TO FIVE

Bros: b-e-a-d-c
The Saturdays: c-a-b-e-d

OUT OF THIS WORLD

1. Sam Ryder
2. Duran Duran
3. Nicki Minaj
4. Savage Garden
5. The Carpenters
6. Air
7. Train
8. Adamski
9. The Rah Band
10. Orchestral Manoeuvres In The Dark (aka OMD)
11. Masked Wolf
12. Ash
13. Stevie McCrorie
14. Inspiral Carpets
15. The Stargazers
16. The Beastie Boys
17. Sarah Brightman & Hot Gossip
18. Jamiroquai
19. Pixie Lott
20. Babylon Zoo

LOOK WHAT YOU MADE ME DO

1. ABC
2. Arctic Monkeys
3. Prince (featuring an uncredited Sheena Easton)
4. Dizzee Rascal
5. Roxette
6. The Hollies
7. The Libertines
8. Slade
9. Go West
10. Storm Queen
11. Diana Ross & Marvin Gaye
12. Geri Halliwell
13. Howard Jones
14. The Temptations

15. Duke Dumont
16. Gene Pitney
17. Ali Campbell
18. Big Country
19. Christina Milian
20. M People

SUPERSTAR SPOTLIGHT: MADONNA

1. *Into The Groove*
2. *The Immaculate Collection*
3. *MDNA*
4. *Me Against The Music*
5. 1998
6. e-d-b-i-h-a-j-f-g-c

TURN BACK THE CLOCK

1. Whitney Houston
2. Cher
3. Moloko
4. Owen Paul
5. Noah And The Whale
6. Status Quo
7. Billie Eilish
8. Booker T & The MGs
9. 2Pac
10. Jimmy James & The Vagabonds
11. The Platters
12. Lisa Stansfield
13. Kylie Minogue
14. Paul Jones
15. Storm
16. George Michael
17. Lizzo
18. Depeche Mode
19. Muse
20. Keane

MONTH BY MONTH: 2010

Jan: Owl City
Feb: Jedward
Mar: *Pass Out*
Apr: Scouting For Girls

May: Fyfe Dangerfield
Jun: *Tears For Fears*
Jul: Beats International
Aug: *Green Light*
Sep: Brandon Flowers
Oct: *Gotta Go Home*
Nov: Take That
Dec: *Many Of Horror*

TOP 10: 2010

1. Ne-Yo
2. *The Club Can't Handle Me*
3. *We No Speak Americano*
4. *Love The Way You Lie*
5. The Wanted
6. *Billionaire*
7. *Airplanes*
8. Eliza Doolittle
9. *One (Your Name)*
10. *California Gurls*

MONTH BY MONTH: 2011

Jan: *Rolling In The Deep*
Feb: Chris Brown
Mar: Nicole Scherzinger
Apr: 1988
May: *The Edge Of Glory*
Jun: *The A Team*
Jul: Beyoncé
Aug: Cher Lloyd
Sep: Rizzle Kicks
Oct: Lana Del Rey
Nov: *Gotta Be You*
Dec: Lou Monte

TOP 10: 2011

1. Example
2. *Give Me Everything*
3. *Right There*
4. Alexandra Stan
5. Aloe Blacc
6. Coldplay
7. *Party Rock Anthem*
8. Bruno Mars

9. *I'm Into You*
10. *Bass Down Low*

MONTH BY MONTH: 2012

Jan: Jessie J
Feb: *Twilight*
Mar: Brian May
Apr: *Call Me Maybe*
May: Scissor Sisters
Jun: *Black Heart*
Jul: Wiz Khalifa
Aug: *One Day Like This*
Sep: Sam And The Womp
Oct: *Skyfall*
Nov: *The Hottest Girl In The World*
Dec: 1988

TOP 10: 2012

1. One Direction
2. Bruno Mars
3. Little Mix
4. *Beneath Your Beautiful*
5. Gabrielle Aplin
6. Robbie Williams
7. PSY
8. *Ho Hey*
9. Rihanna
10. McFly

MONTH BY MONTH: 2013

Jan: Shontelle
Feb: *Thrift Shop*
Mar: Bastille
Apr: 1994
May: *Get Lucky*
Jun: Black Sabbath
Jul: Avril Lavigne
Aug: Miley Cyrus
Sep: *Roar*
Oct: OneRepublic
Nov: 2004
Dec: Demi Lovato

TOP 10: 2013

1. Avicii
2. *Blurred Lines*
3. John Newman
4. *I Love It*
5. Bang Bang
6. *La La La*
7. *Reload*
8. Selena Gomez
9. *Jack*
10. *Let Her Go*

MONTH BY MONTH: 2014

Jan: Ke$ha
Feb: Paramore
Mar: A Great Big World
Apr: John Legend
May: *Rise Like A Phoenix*
Jun: Rik Mayall
Jul: *Me And My Broken Heart*
Aug: Nico & Vinz
Sep: Paloma Faith
Oct: *All About That Bass*
Nov: 1989
Dec: *Something I Need*

TOP 10: 2014

1. *Rude*
2. *Crazy Stupid Love*
3. *Faded*
4. Ella Henderson
5. *Hopeful*
6. George Ezra
7. *Problem*
8. Charli XCX
9. *It's My Birthday*
10. *Kisses For Breakfast*

MONTH BY MONTH: 2015

Jan: *Uptown Funk*
Feb: Hozier
Mar: James Bay
Apr: *Hold My Hand*

May: Lunchmoney Lewis
Jun: *Shut Up And Dance*
Jul: Lost Frequencies
Aug: Cilla Black
Sep: 1984
Oct: Jamie Lawson
Nov: Fleur East
Dec: The Lewisham &
Greenwich NHS Choir

TOP 10: 2015

1. Justin Bieber
2. *Locked Away*
3. Sam Smith
4. *Alone No More*
5. Ellie Goulding
6. *Runnin' (Lose It All)*
7. Sigala
8. Drake
9. *How Deep Is Your Love*
10. *Do It Again*

MONTH BY MONTH: 2016

Jan: Shawn Mendes
Feb: *7 Years*
Mar: *I Took A Pill In Ibiza*
Apr: *Lush Life*
May: Justin Timberlake
Jun: Louisa Johnson
Jul: Rihanna
Aug: Robyn
Sep: Twenty One Pilots
Oct: *This Town*
Nov: The Beatles *(Black Beatles)*
Dec: *When Christmas
Comes Around*

TOP 10: 2016

1. Little Mix
2. James Arthur
3. *Closer*
4. The Weeknd featuring
Daft Punk
5. *Starving*

6. *The Greatest*
7. Ariana Grande featuring
Nicki Minaj
8. Calvin Harris
9. *Let Me Love You*
10. Bruno Mars

MONTH BY MONTH: 2017

Jan: Rag'n'Bone Man
Feb: Stormzy
Mar: *Chained To The Rhythm*
Apr: Harry Styles *(Sign
Of The Times)*
May: Luis Fonsi featuring Daddy
Yankee & Justin Bieber
Jun: 1970
Jul: *Wild Thoughts*
Aug: *New Rules*
Sep: CNCO
Oct: *Love Island*
Nov: Big Shaq
Dec: Eminem

TOP 10: 2017

1. *Havana*
2. *Rockstar*
3. *Silence*
4. *Lonely Together*
5. *Dusk Till Dawn*
6. Ed Sheeran
7. Sam Smith
8. *Finders Keepers*
9. Charlie Puth
10. *Mi Gente*

MONTH BY MONTH: 2018

Jan: Ramz
Feb: Nine
Mar: *Feel It Still*
Apr: *The Greatest Showman*
May: Childish Gambino
Jun: 5 Seconds Of Summer
Jul: 1996
Aug: *Body*

Sep: Cardi B
Oct: Silk City
Nov: Bradley Cooper
Dec: 1985

TOP 10: 2018

1. George Ezra
2. *Solo*
3. Anne-Marie
4. Jess Glynne
5. *Sad*
6. Years & Years
7. Post Malone
8. *I Like It*
9. Tom Walker
10. Calvin Harris & Dua Lipa

MONTH BY MONTH: 2019

Jan: Ava Max
Feb: *Break Up With Your Girlfriend I'm Bored*
Mar: Jonas Brothers
Apr: Billie Eilish
May: Panic At The Disco
Jun: Lewis Capaldi
Jul: Fifth Harmony
Aug: *Three*
Sep: 1986
Oct: Burna Boy
Nov: Lizzo
Dec: *You're In My Heart*

TOP 10: 2019

1. *Dance Monkey*
2. Regard
3. Post Malone
4. *South Of The Border*
5. Travis Scott
6. Lewis Capaldi
7. Dermot Kennedy
8. *Buss Down*
9. *Be Honest*
10. Maroon 5

HEY LORD, DON'T ASK ME QUESTIONS

1. Travis
2. Duran Duran
3. Janet Jackson
4. Tubeway Army
5. R.E.M.
6. The Honeycombs
7. DJ Pied Piper And The Masters Of Ceremonies
8. Mary Hopkin
9. The Offspring
10. Adam Faith
11. Keane
12. Alexei Sayle
13. Andy Stewart
14. Hurricane Smith
15. Lita Roza
16. Arctic Monkeys
17. Tom Jones
18. Bryan Adams
19. Aretha Franklin
20. Gwen Stefani

THE WEEK AHEAD

1. The Cure
2. Blondie
3. Whigfield
4. The Boomtown Rats
5. Shed Seven
6. Melanie
7. Hedgehoppers Anonymous
8. Morrissey
9. Elton John
10. Jess Glynne
11. Lil' Dicky featuring Chris Brown
12. The Undertones
13. The Stylistics
14. Will Young
15. Barry Blue
16. The Small Faces
17. B.B.E.
18. The Monkees

19. Chairmen Of The Board
20. Barenaked Ladies

NUMBER 1 ALBUMS

1. Mike Oldfield
2. Alanis Morissette
3. Coldplay
4. Lewis Capaldi
5. Frank Sinatra
6. The Rolling Stones
7. Paul Simon
8. East 17
9. Bruno Mars
10. The Beatles
11. Adam And The Ants
12. Arctic Monkeys
13. ABBA
14. Travis
15. Neil Young
16. Wet Wet Wet
17. Beyoncé
18. Jason Donovan
19. The Moody Blues
20. Olivia Rodrigo
21. George Harrison
22. Pink Floyd
23. Mika
24. Bob Dylan
25. Adele
26. The Beautiful South
27. Paolo Nutini
28. Dr. Feelgood
29. Dua Lipa
30. The White Stripes
31. Rod Stewart
32. David Bowie
33. The Small Faces
34. Kings Of Leon
35. Tubeway Army
36. The Cranberries
37. Howard Jones
38. Radiohead
39. Paul Weller
40. The Streets

HIP-HOP LEGENDS

1. Eminem
2. Jay-Z
3. Beastie Boys
4. Wu-Tang Clan
5. Public Enemy
6. A Tribe Called Quest
7. Bone Thugs-N-Harmony
8. The Sugarhill Gang
9. De La Soul
10. Grandmaster Flash &
    The Furious Five
11. Cypress Hill
12. Ice-T
13. Outkast
14. Run-DMC
15. N.W.A.
16. Eric B & Rakim
17. Dr Dre
18. 2Pac
19. LL Cool J
20. Snoop Doggy Dogg

HIT AFTER HIT / ONE TO FIVE

Eminem: d-e-b-c-a
Sean Paul: e-d-b-a-c

HIT AFTER HIT / ONE TO FIVE

Drake: a-c-d-e-b
Craig David: e-a-b-c-d

LITTLE THINGS MEAN A LOT

1. Fleetwood Mac
2. Elvis vs JXL
3. Electric Light Orchestra
4. Erasure
5. Billy J. Kramer with
    The Dakotas
6. The Beautiful South
7. One Direction
8. The Sweet
9. Nina & Frederik
10. The Smurfs

11. DJ Luck & MC Neat
12. Green Jelly
13. Tommy Steele
14. Wings
15. Leapy Lee
16. Tina Charles
17. Tom Grennan
18. The Monkees
19. JoJo
20. The Rolling Stones

SUPERSTAR SPOTLIGHT: BEYONCÉ

1. 1998
2. *Charlie's Angels*
3. Samantha Sang
4. Three weeks
5. Shakira
6. e-c-d-b-a

HIT AFTER HIT / ONE TO FIVE

Taylor Swift: a-d-b-e-c
Mariah Carey: e-b-d-a-c

SOMETHING IN THE AIR

1. Prince
2. Fleetwood Mac
3. Nelly Furtado
4. Oasis
5. Steven Houghton
6. Annie Lennox
7. The Tweets
8. Moony
9. Manfred Mann
10. Madness
11. Pearl Carr & Teddy Johnson
12. Snowy White
13. Eminem
14. The Ramblers (from The Abbey Hey Junior School)
15. Cast
16. Sweet People
17. Kid Creole & The Coconuts
18. Seal

19. Little Mix
20. T.Rex

HIT AFTER HIT / ONE TO FIVE

Dua Lipa: c-a-d-e-b
Usher: a-e-d-b-c

WE ARE FAMILY

1. Level 42
2. ABBA
3. St. Winifred's School Choir
4. George Michael
5. Kid Creole & The Coconuts
6. Boyzone
7. Avicii
8. Slade
9. Stephanie Beatriz Olga Merediz and The Cast Of Encanto
10. Boney M
11. Rizzle Kicks
12. Clive Dunn
13. Luther Vandross
14. Madness
15. Pixie Lott
16. Dana Dawson
17. The Marmalade
18. Paul Simon
19. Black Grape
20. Genesis
21. Terence Trent D'Arby
22. P!nk
23. Paul Nicholas
24. Daryl Hall & John Oates
25. Train
26. Eddie Calvert
27. Feargal Sharkey
28. The Rolling Stones
29. The Drifters
30. Cliff Richard
31. Neil Reid
32. Black Eyed Peas
33. Thompson Twins
34. Chicory Tip
35. Doctor Hook & The

Medicine Show
36. Nat King Cole
37. Modern Talking
38. Tears For Fears
39. Free
40. Sly & The Family Stone

SUPERSTAR SPOTLIGHT: ED SHEERAN

1. 2011
2. *Love Yourself*
3. The Chainsmokers & Coldplay (their song at Number 7 was *Something Just Like This*)
4. 4. 7 years and 1 month (June 2014 to July 2021)
5. Liam Payne
6. b-a-e-d-c

HIT AFTER HIT / ONE TO FIVE

New Kids On The Block: e-d-c-b-a
Justin Bieber: d-b-a-e-c

MONTH BY MONTH: 2020

Jan: Juice Wrld
Feb: *The Box*
Mar: *Roses*
Apr: 1963
May: *Times Like These*
Jun: Lady Gaga & Ariana Grande
Jul: Bob Dylan
Aug: Six
Sep: *You Broke Me First*
Oct: Headie One
Nov: *Stop Crying Your Heart Out*
Dec: 1994

TOP 10: 2020

1. *Rockstar*
2. Drake
3. Doja Cat
4. *Stuck With U*

5. *Death Bed*
6. 6ix9ine
7. The Weeknd
8. *Rover*
9. Megan Thee Stallion
10. AJ Tracey featuring Mostack

MONTH BY MONTH: 2021

Jan: *Whoopty*
Feb: *Love Story*
Mar: *Latest Trends*
Apr: Nathan Evans
May: Royal Blood
Jun: Italian
Jul: *Holiday*
Aug: The Killers
Sep: *Don't Shut Me Down*
Oct: BTS
Nov: *Overpass Graffiti*
Dec: 1962

TOP 10: 2021

1. *Body*
2. Olivia Rodrigo
3. *Kiss Me More*
4. Lil Nas X
5. The Weeknd
6. *Bed*
7. *Peaches*
8. *Friday*
9. *Anywhere Away From Here*
10. Tom Grennan

HIT AFTER HIT / ONE TO FIVE

The Killers: d-e-c-b-a
Leona Lewis: d-b-e-a-c

SUPERSTAR SPOTLIGHT: ADELE

1. 19+21+25+30 = 95
2. Three
3. *(To Your New Lover)*
4. 2012

5. Bob Dylan
6. d-e-b-a-c

HIT AFTER HIT / ONE TO FIVE

Human League: d-b-e-c-a
The Beach Boys: d-b-a-e-c

HIT AFTER HIT / ONE TO FIVE

Kool And The Gang: a-b-e-c-d
Whitney Houston: c-b-a-e-d

HIT AFTER HIT / ONE TO FIVE

Shakin' Stevens: d-e-c-b-a
Britney Spears: b-a-d-c-e

CHRISTMAS NUMBER 1s?

Only Songs 4 (Dickie Valentine), 13 (Mud), 16 (Shakin' Stevens) and 17 (Slade) were genuine Christmas Number 1s on the Official Singles Chart.

Mariah Carey's 1994 hit *All I Want For Christmas* finally got to Number 1 in 2020 but it was knocked off by LadBaby with *Don't Stop Me Eatin'* when the festive chart was announced on Christmas Day itself.

Last Christmas the 1984 classic by Wham! eventually reached Number 1 on the first Official Singles Chart of 2022 (announced on Friday 31 December 2021) but failed to top the chart a week earlier because the collaborative effort by LadBaby featuring Ed Sheeran and Elton John got there first with *Sausage Rolls For Everyone*.

WHEN YOU'RE GONE

1. The Beatles
2. Tin Tin Out featuring Shelley Nelson
3. Gloria Gaynor
4. Bill Haley & His Comets
5. Soft Cell
6. Jimmy Ruffin
7. The Searchers
8. Blur
9. Karl Denver
10. INXS
11. The Manhattans
12. Cliff Richard
13. Simply Red
14. Johnny Mathis
15. Honeyz
16. Roger Whittaker
17. A1
18. Peter Cook and Dudley Moore
19. Placebo
20. Spice Girls